Anatomy & Physiology

Coloring Workbook

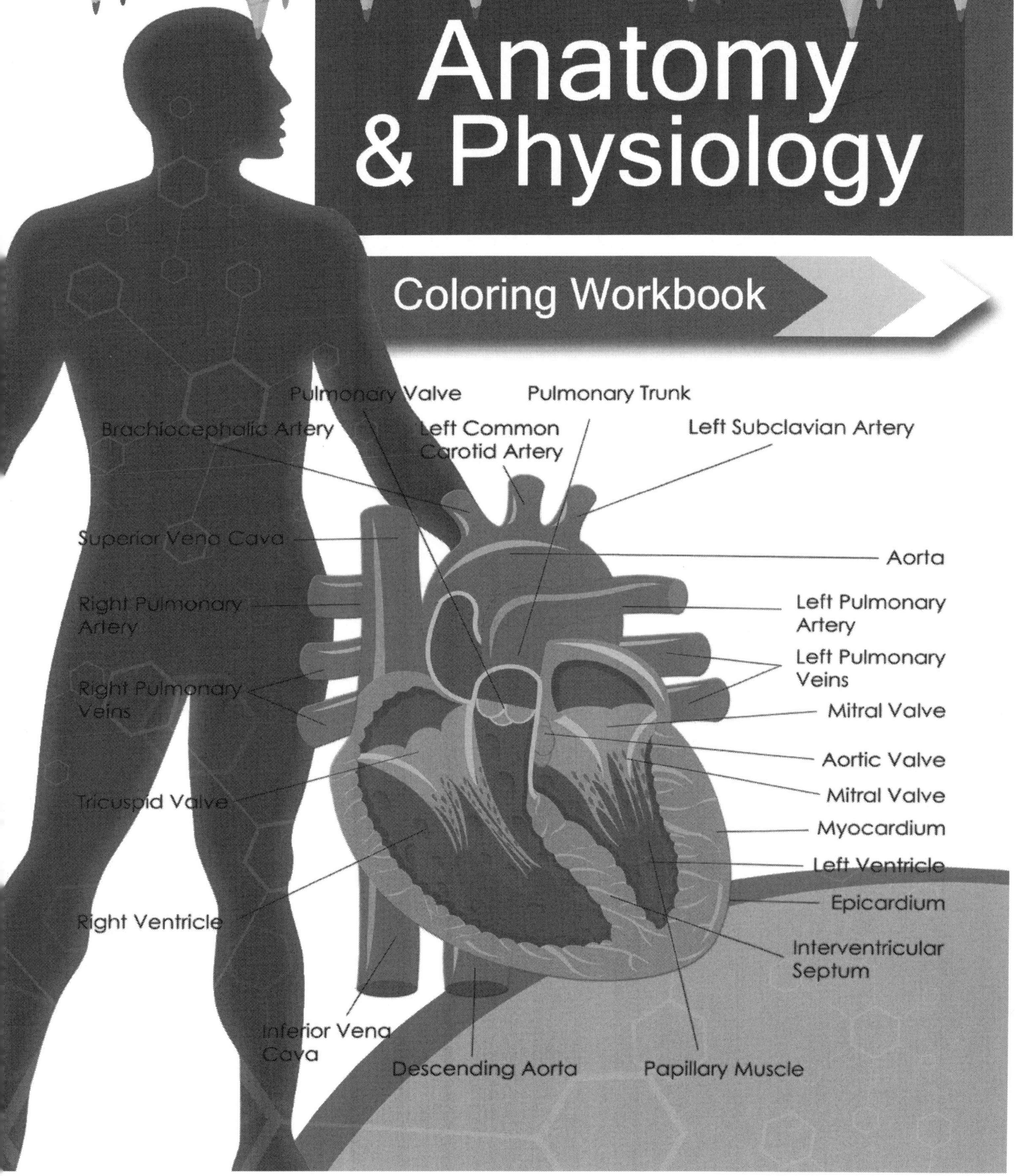

COLOR TEST PAGE

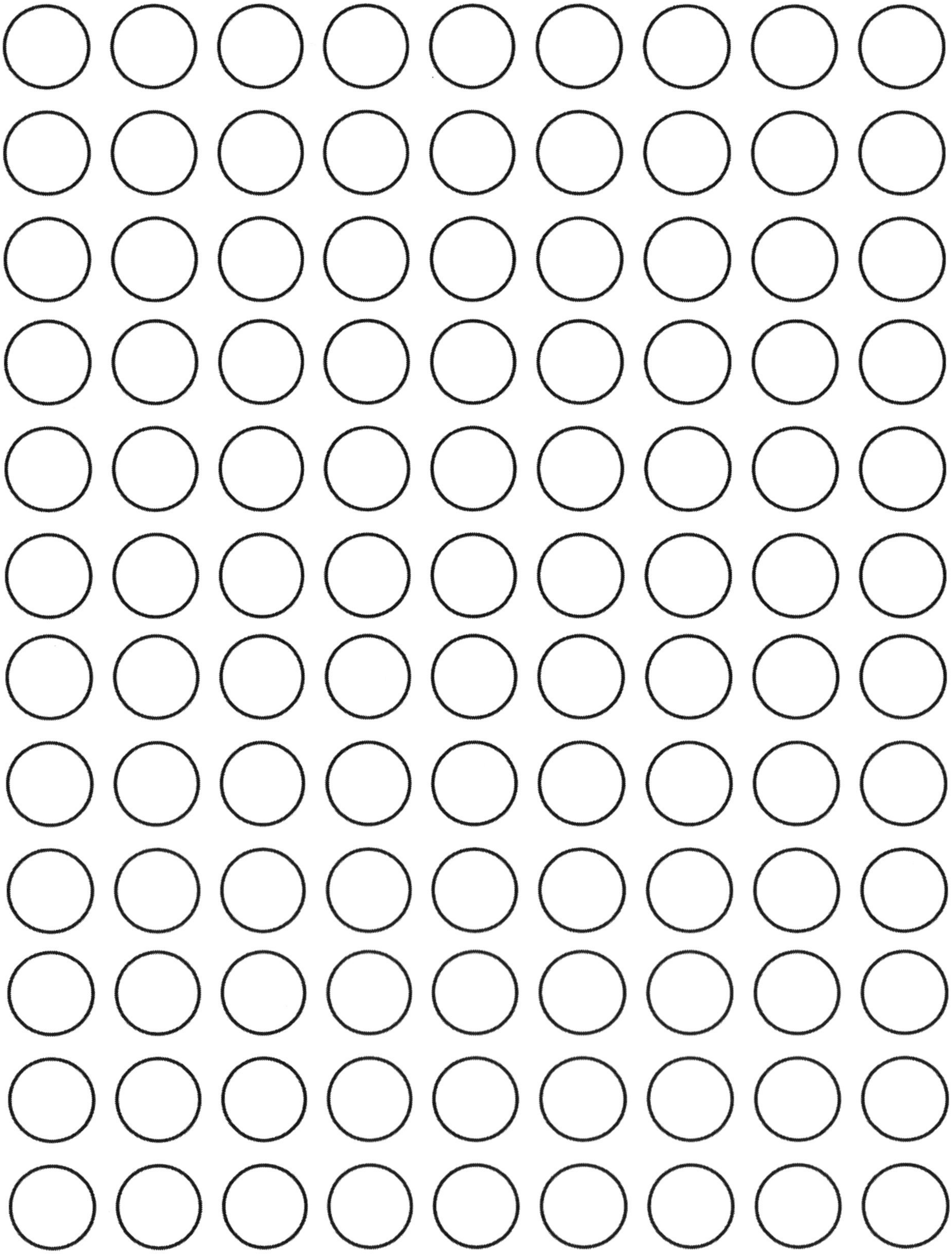

COLOR TEST PAGE

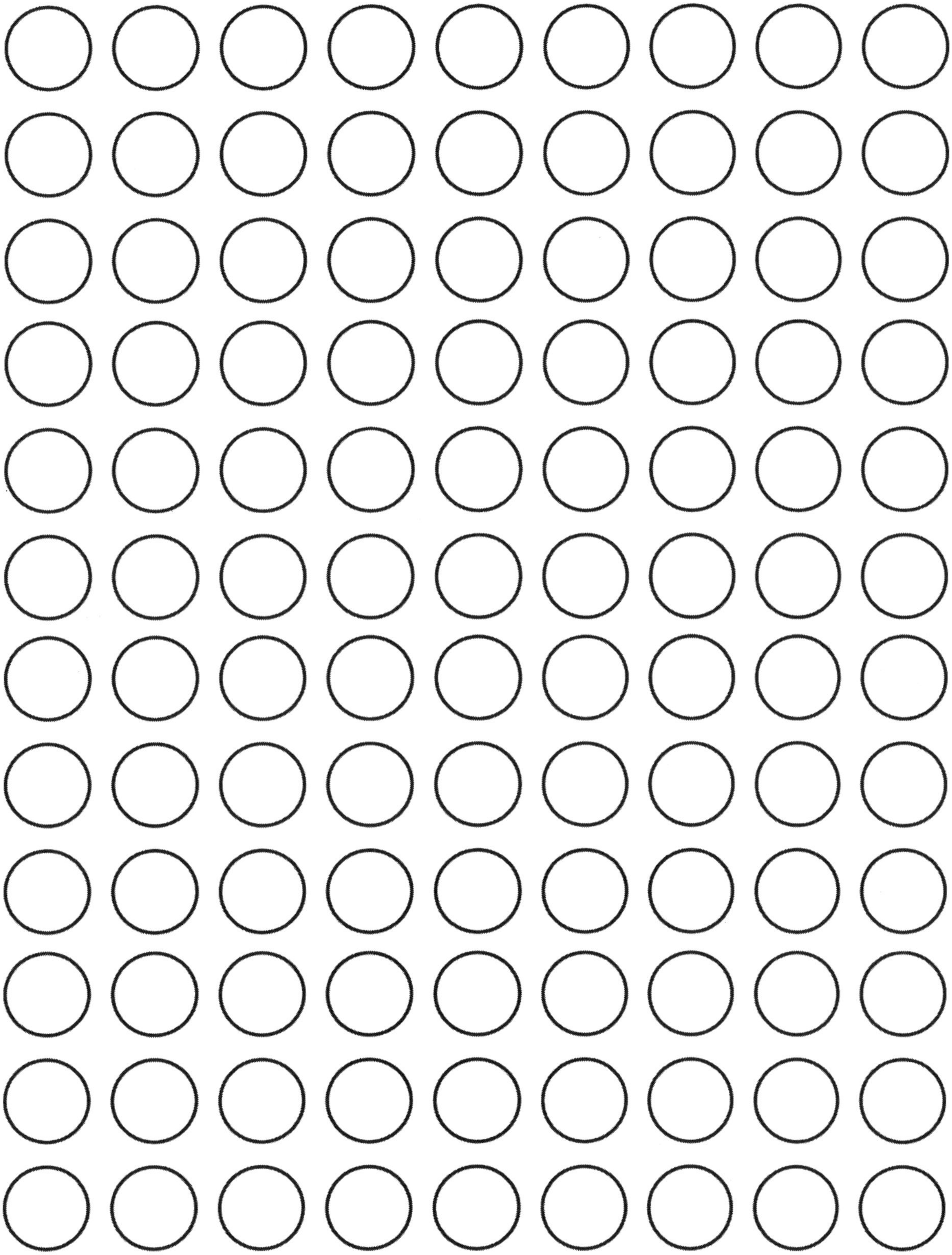

SKULL

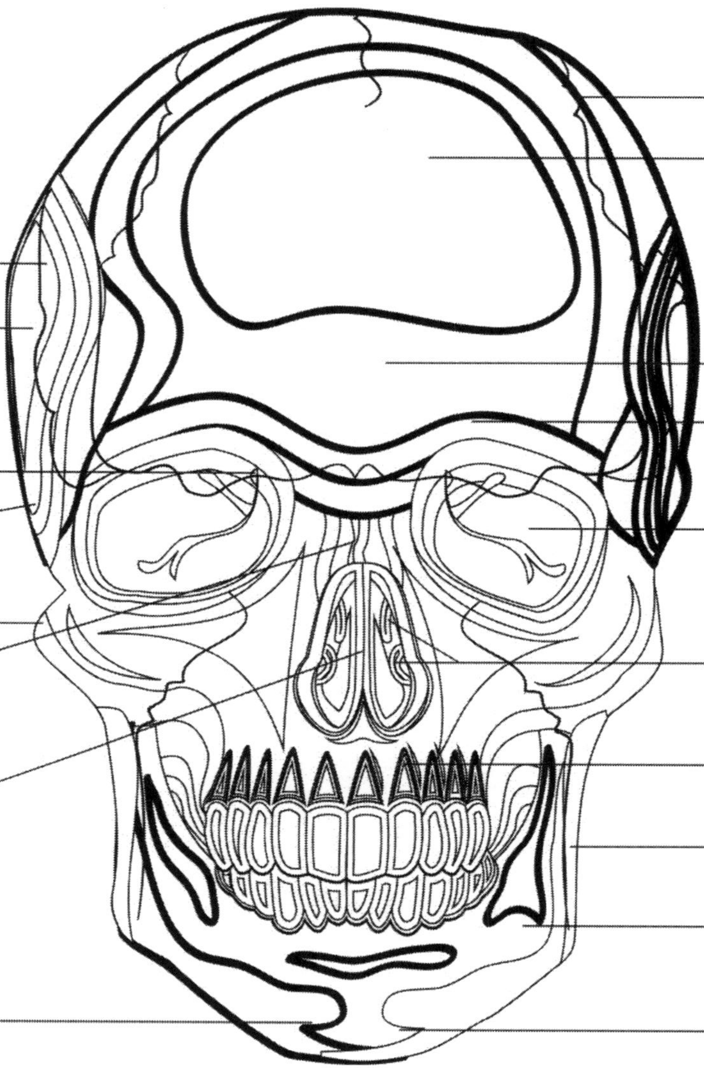

Coronal Suture
Frontal Bone
Temporal Bone
Parietal Bone
Glabella
Sphenoid Foramen
Optic Canal
Temporal Bone
Sphenoid Bone
Zygomatic Arch
Nasal Concha
Nasal Bone
Aveolar Process
Ethmoid Bone
Ramus
Mandible
Mental Tuberosity
Mental Protruberance

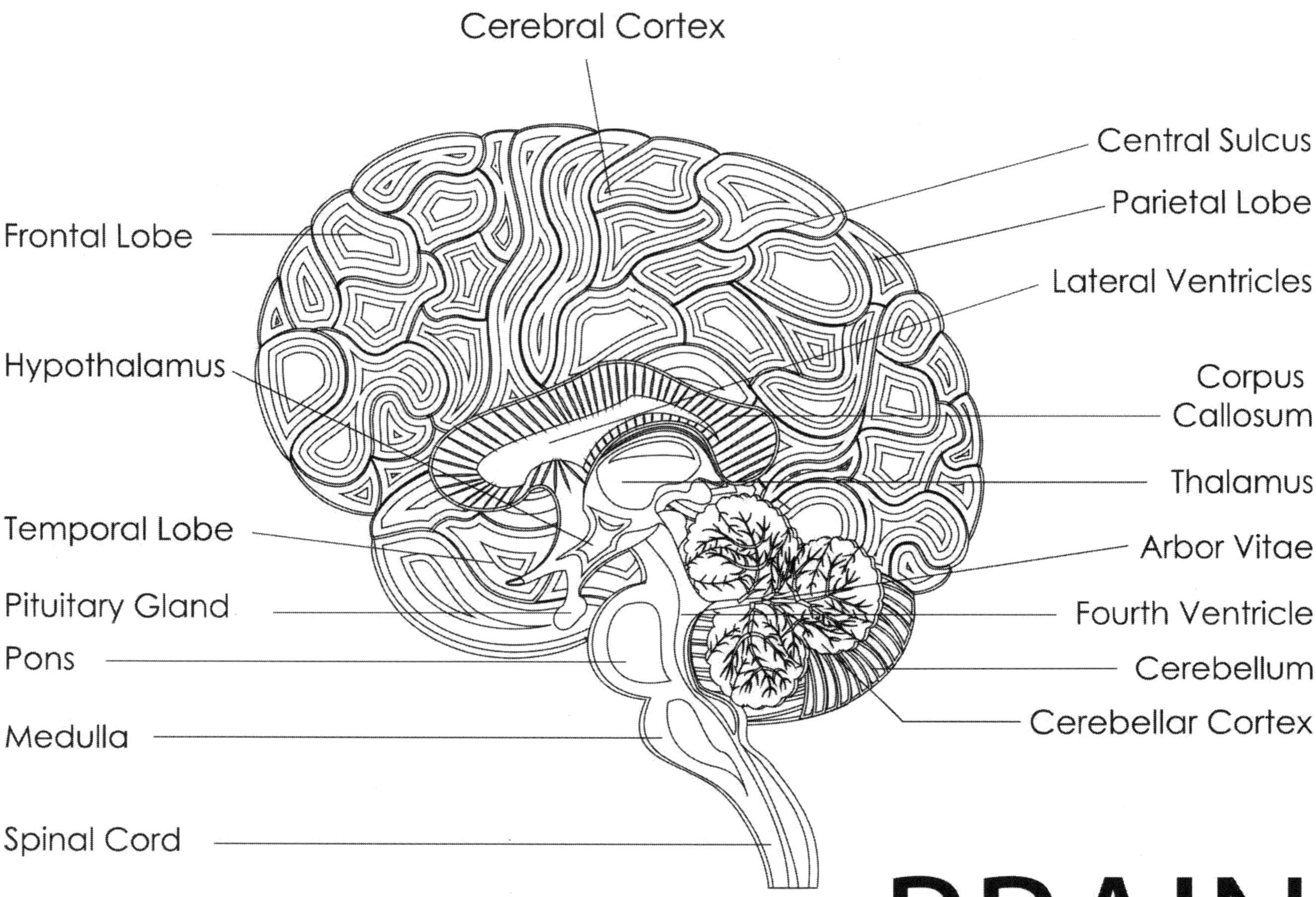
Cerebral Cortex
Central Sulcus
Parietal Lobe
Frontal Lobe
Lateral Ventricles
Hypothalamus
Corpus Callosum
Thalamus
Temporal Lobe
Arbor Vitae
Pituitary Gland
Fourth Ventricle
Pons
Cerebellum
Cerebellar Cortex
Medulla
Spinal Cord

BRAIN

EYE

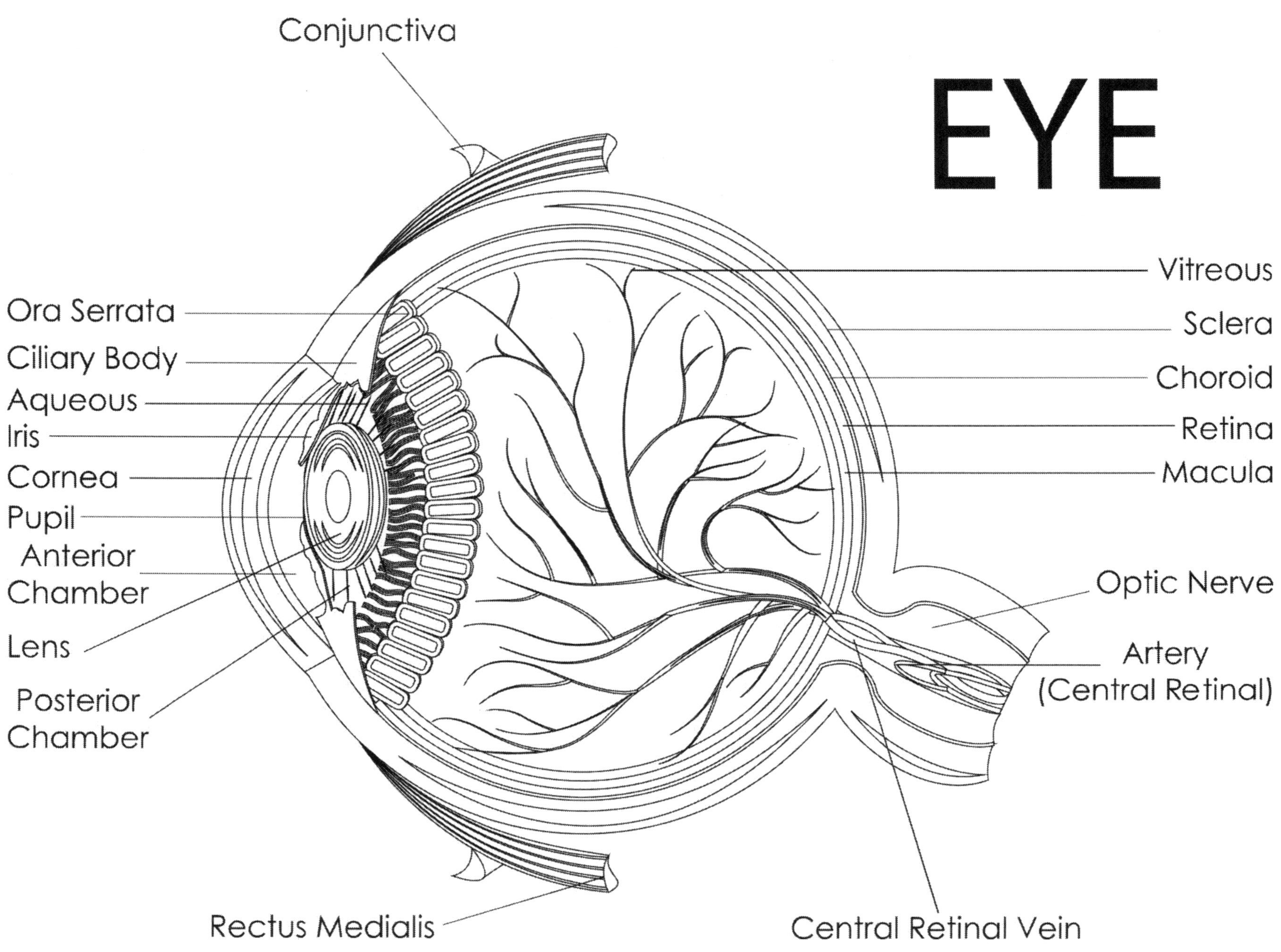
Conjunctiva
Ora Serrata
Ciliary Body
Aqueous
Iris
Cornea
Pupil
Anterior Chamber
Lens
Posterior Chamber
Rectus Medialis
Vitreous
Sclera
Choroid
Retina
Macula
Optic Nerve
Artery (Central Retinal)
Central Retinal Vein

MOUTH

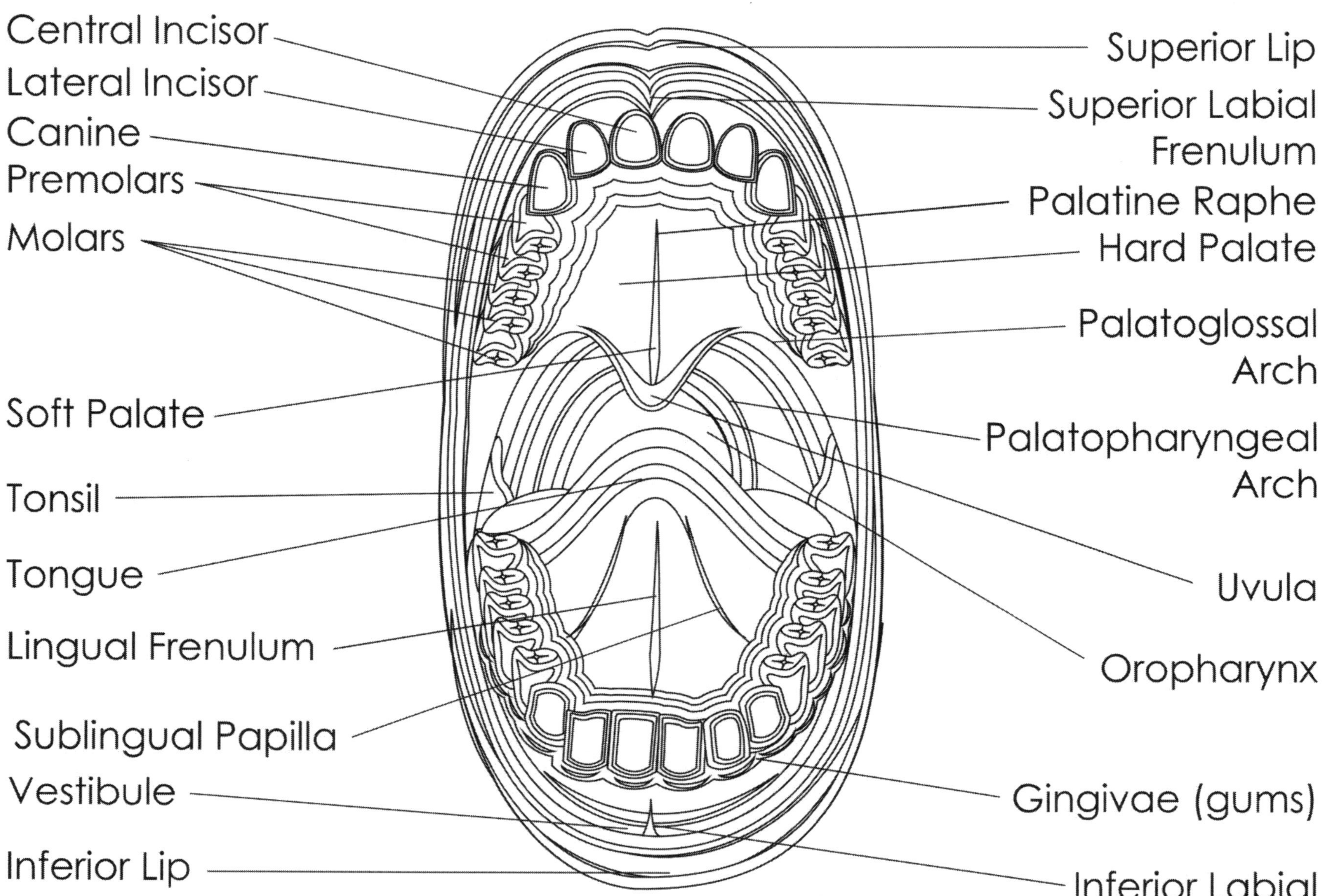

Central Incisor
Lateral Incisor
Canine
Premolars
Molars
Soft Palate
Tonsil
Tongue
Lingual Frenulum
Sublingual Papilla
Vestibule
Inferior Lip
Superior Lip
Superior Labial Frenulum
Palatine Raphe
Hard Palate
Palatoglossal Arch
Palatopharyngeal Arch
Uvula
Oropharynx
Gingivae (gums)
Inferior Labial Frenulum

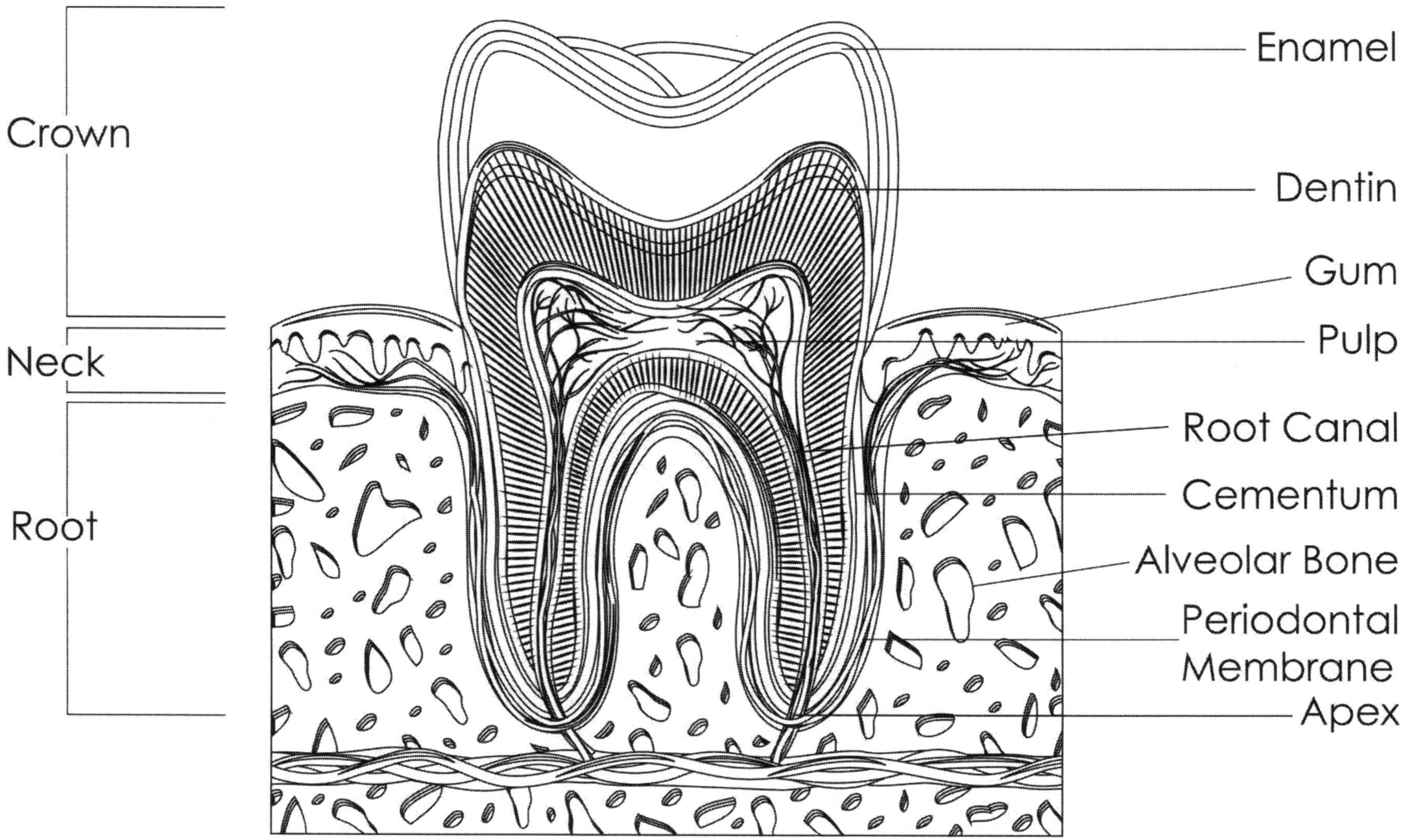
Crown
Neck
Root
Enamel
Dentin
Gum
Pulp
Root Canal
Cementum
Alveolar Bone
Periodontal
Membrane
Apex

TOOTH

TONGUE

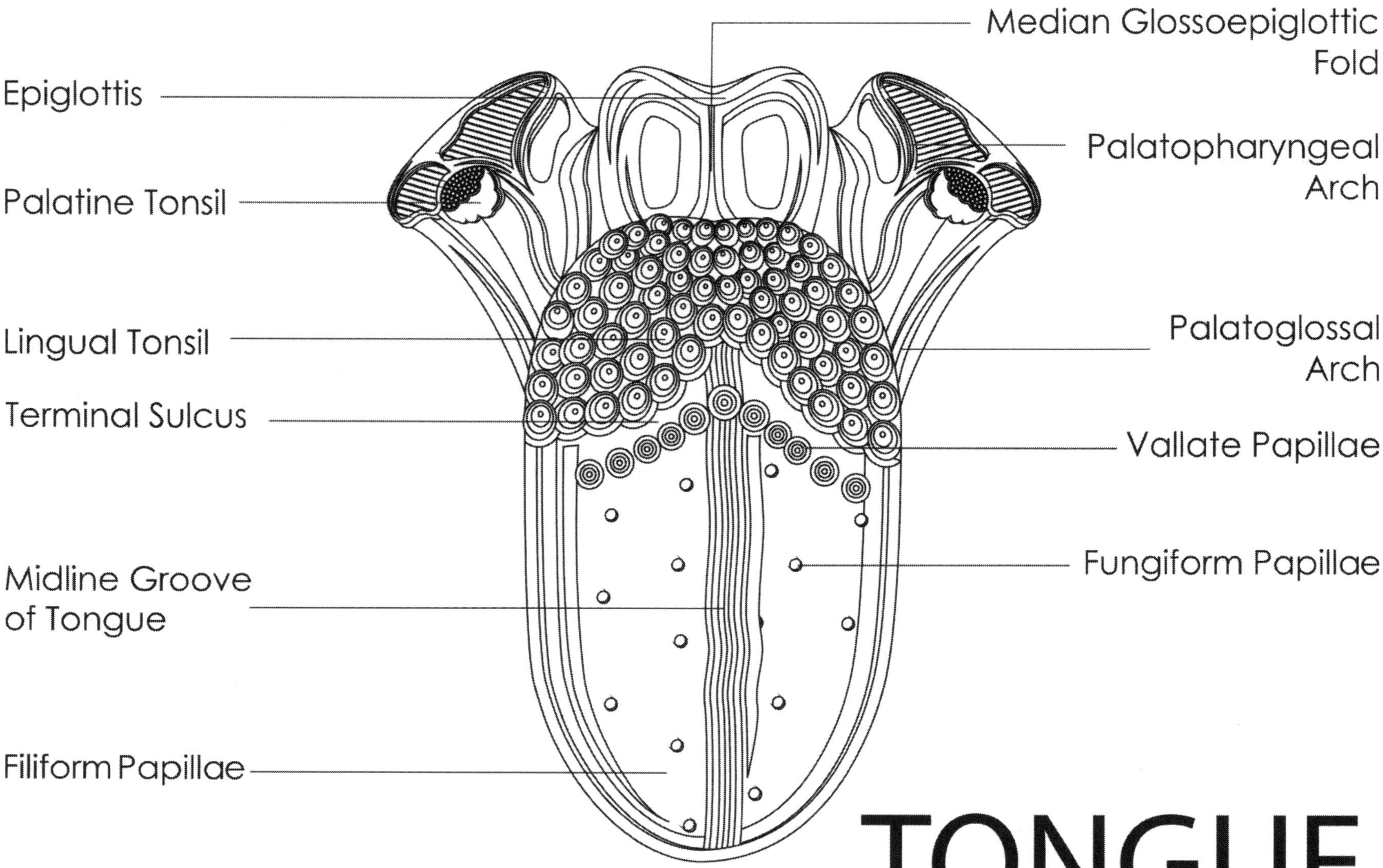
Median Glossoepiglottic Fold
Epiglottis
Palatopharyngeal Arch
Palatine Tonsil
Palatoglossal Arch
Lingual Tonsil
Terminal Sulcus
Vallate Papillae
Fungiform Papillae
Midline Groove of Tongue
Filiform Papillae

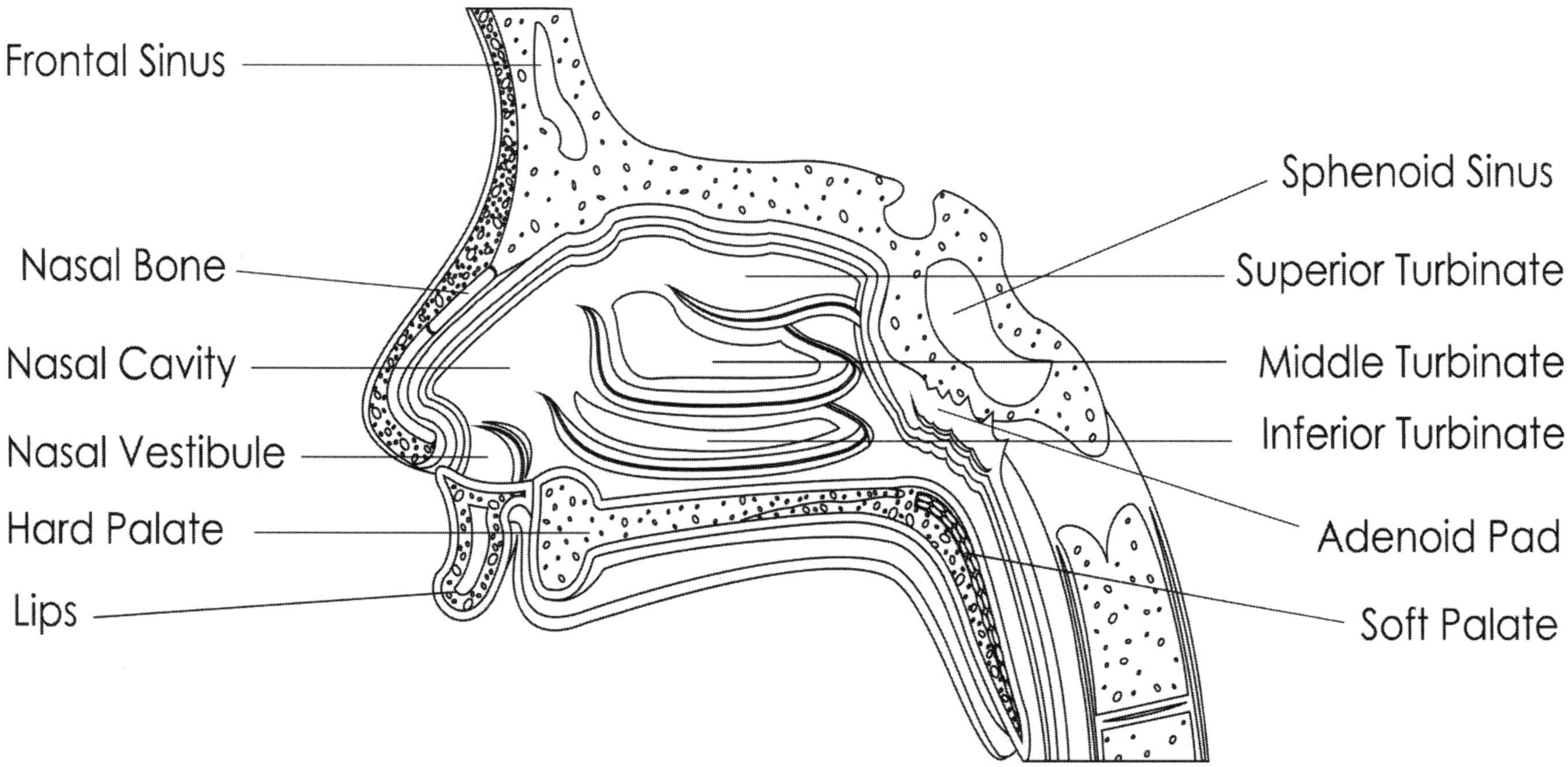
Frontal Sinus
Nasal Bone
Nasal Cavity
Nasal Vestibule
Hard Palate
Lips
Sphenoid Sinus
Superior Turbinate
Middle Turbinate
Inferior Turbinate
Adenoid Pad
Soft Palate

NOSE

THROAT

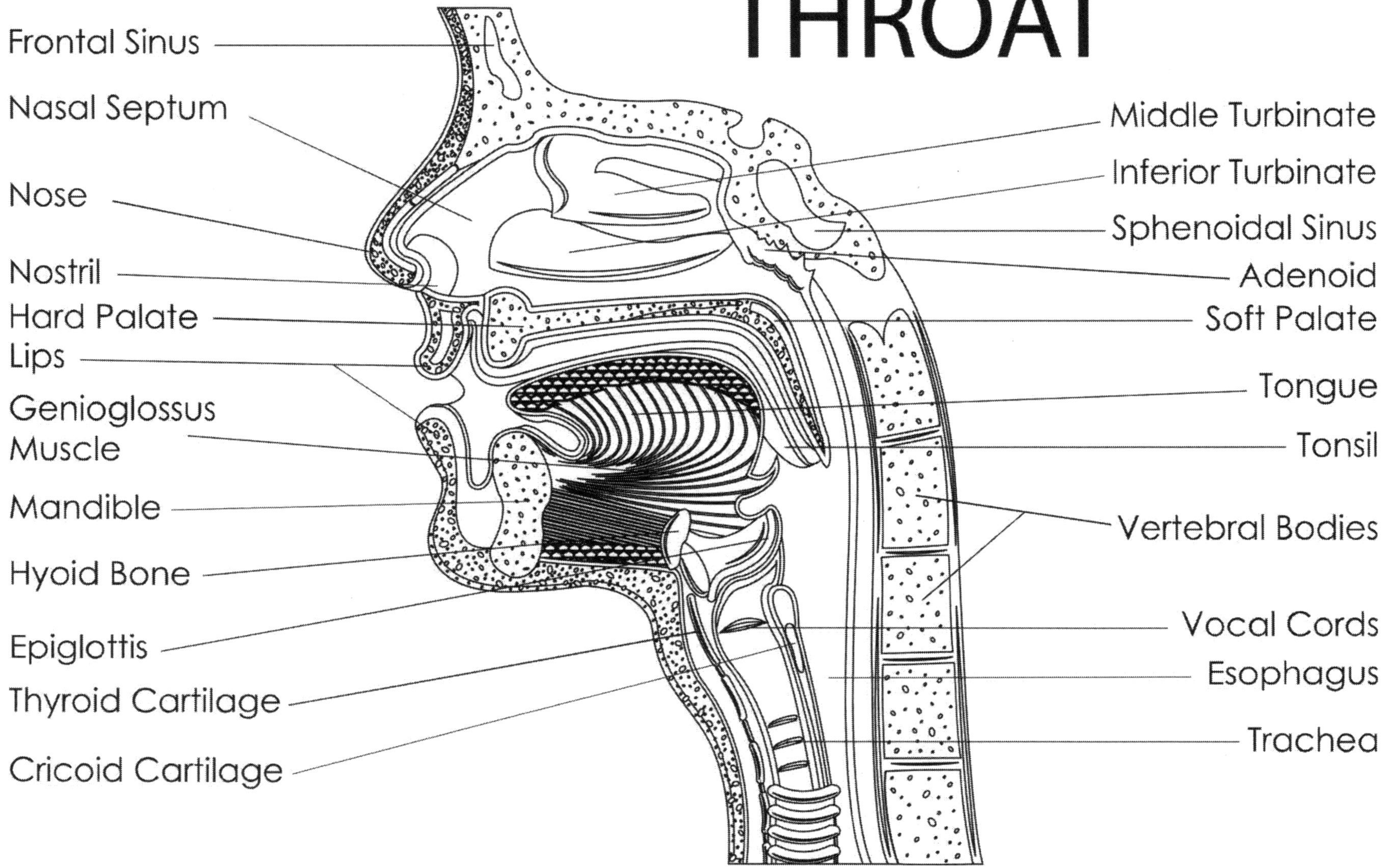

Frontal Sinus
Nasal Septum
Nose
Nostril
Hard Palate
Lips
Genioglossus Muscle
Mandible
Hyoid Bone
Epiglottis
Thyroid Cartilage
Cricoid Cartilage
Middle Turbinate
Inferior Turbinate
Sphenoidal Sinus
Adenoid
Soft Palate
Tongue
Tonsil
Vertebral Bodies
Vocal Cords
Esophagus
Trachea

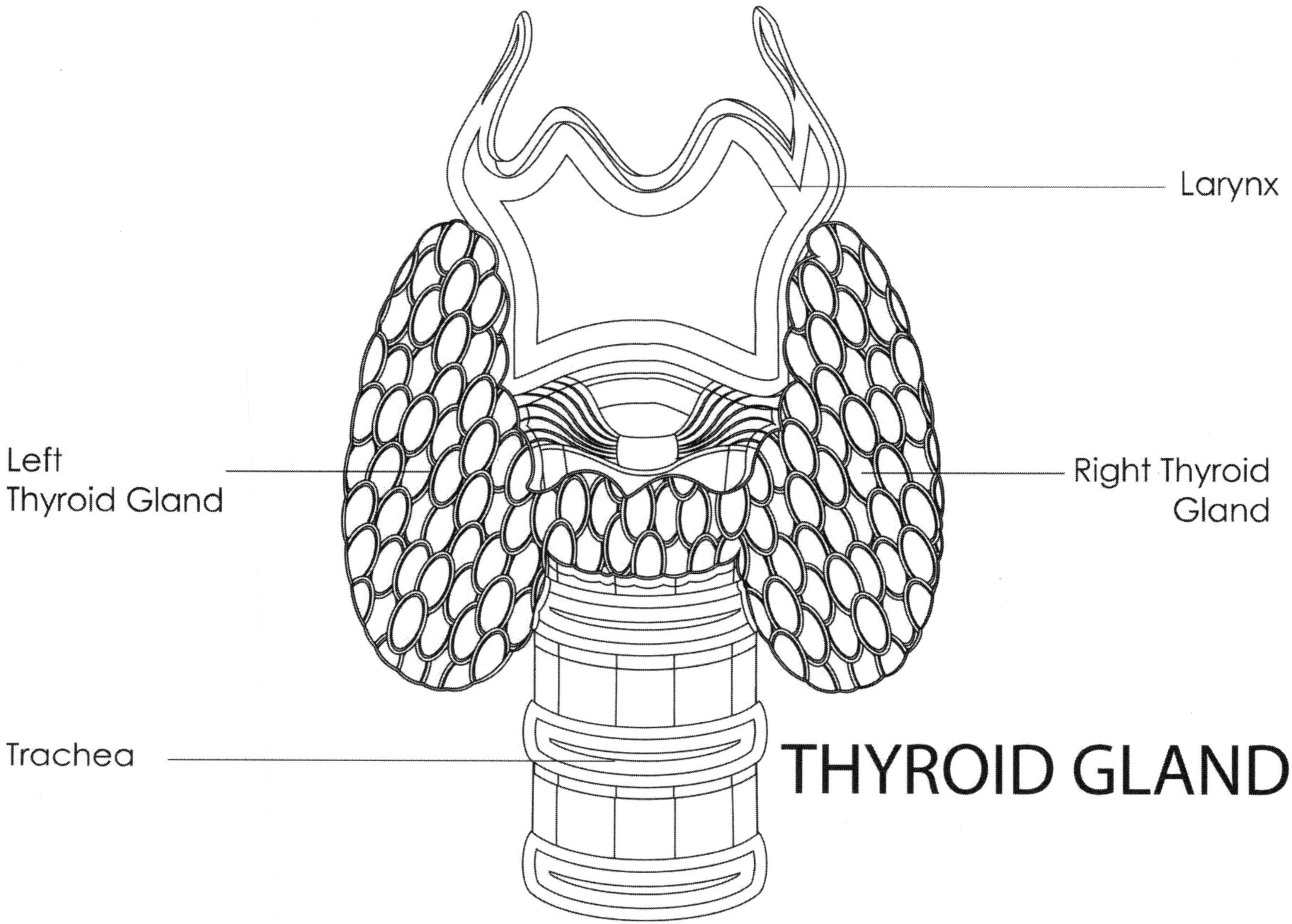

THYROID GLAND

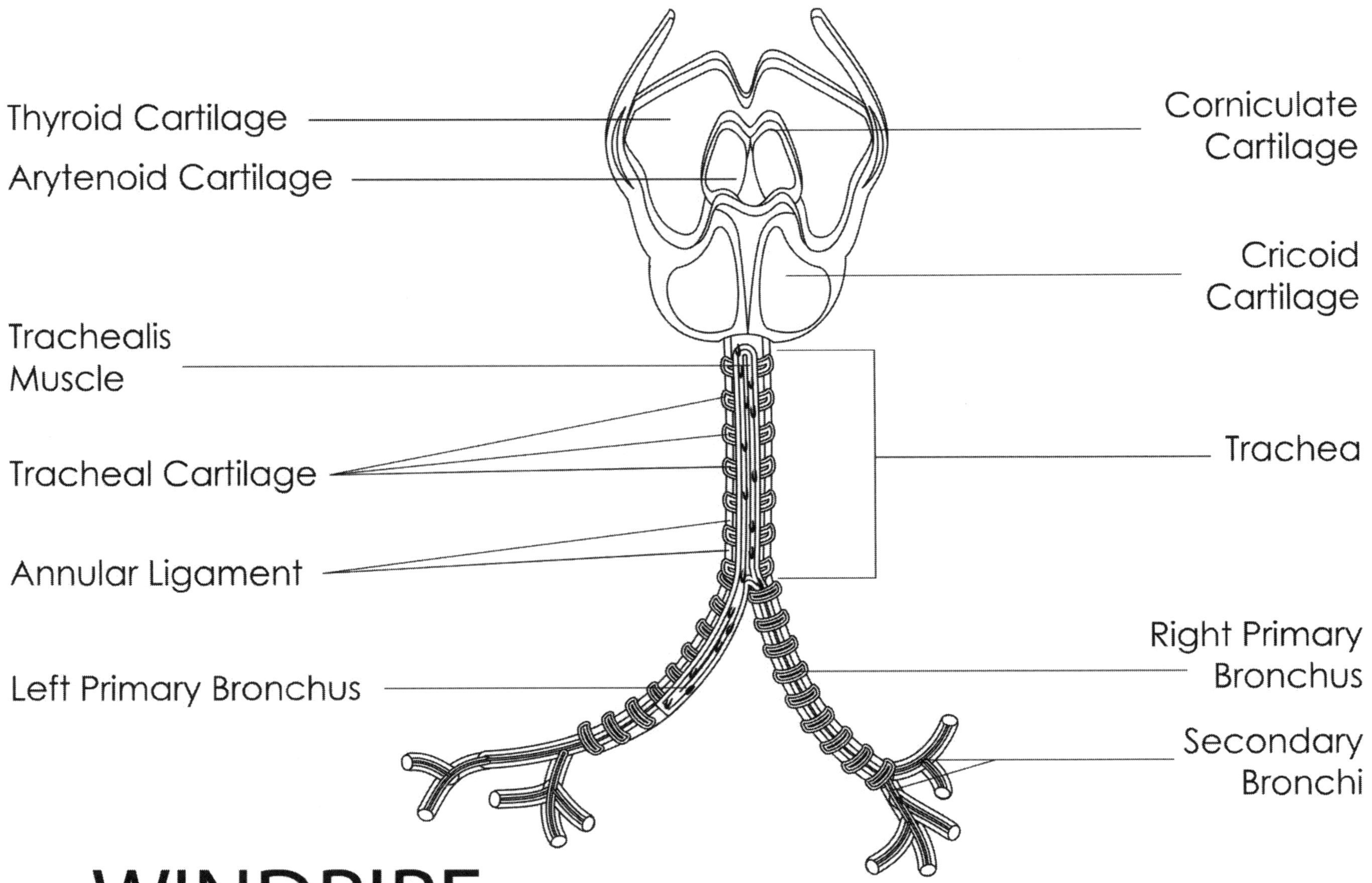
Thyroid Cartilage
Arytenoid Cartilage
Trachealis Muscle
Tracheal Cartilage
Annular Ligament
Left Primary Bronchus
Corniculate Cartilage
Cricoid Cartilage
Trachea
Right Primary Bronchus
Secondary Bronchi

WINDPIPE

LARYNX

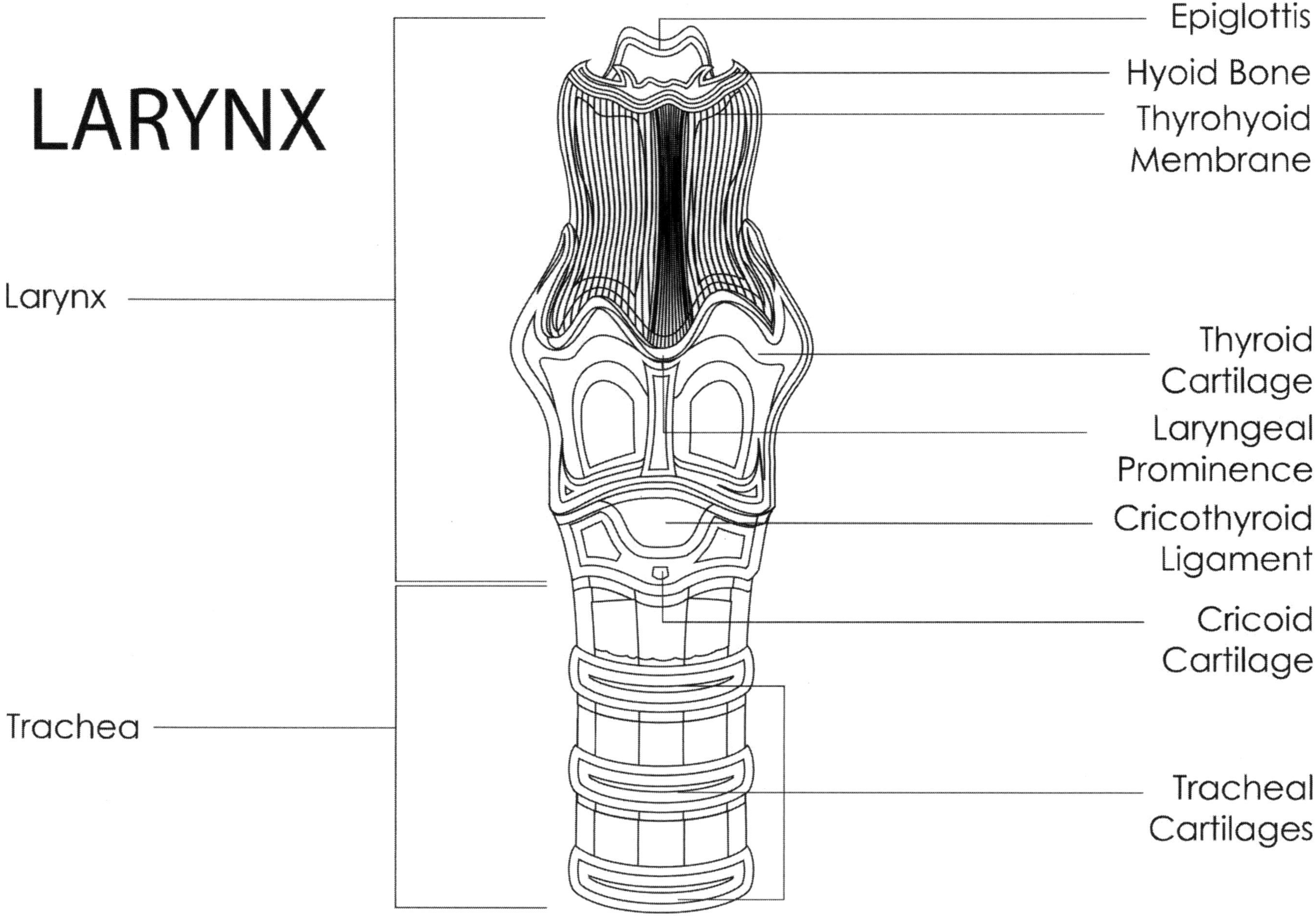

Epiglottis
Hyoid Bone
Thyrohyoid Membrane
Larynx
Thyroid Cartilage
Laryngeal Prominence
Cricothyroid Ligament
Cricoid Cartilage
Trachea
Tracheal Cartilages

EAR

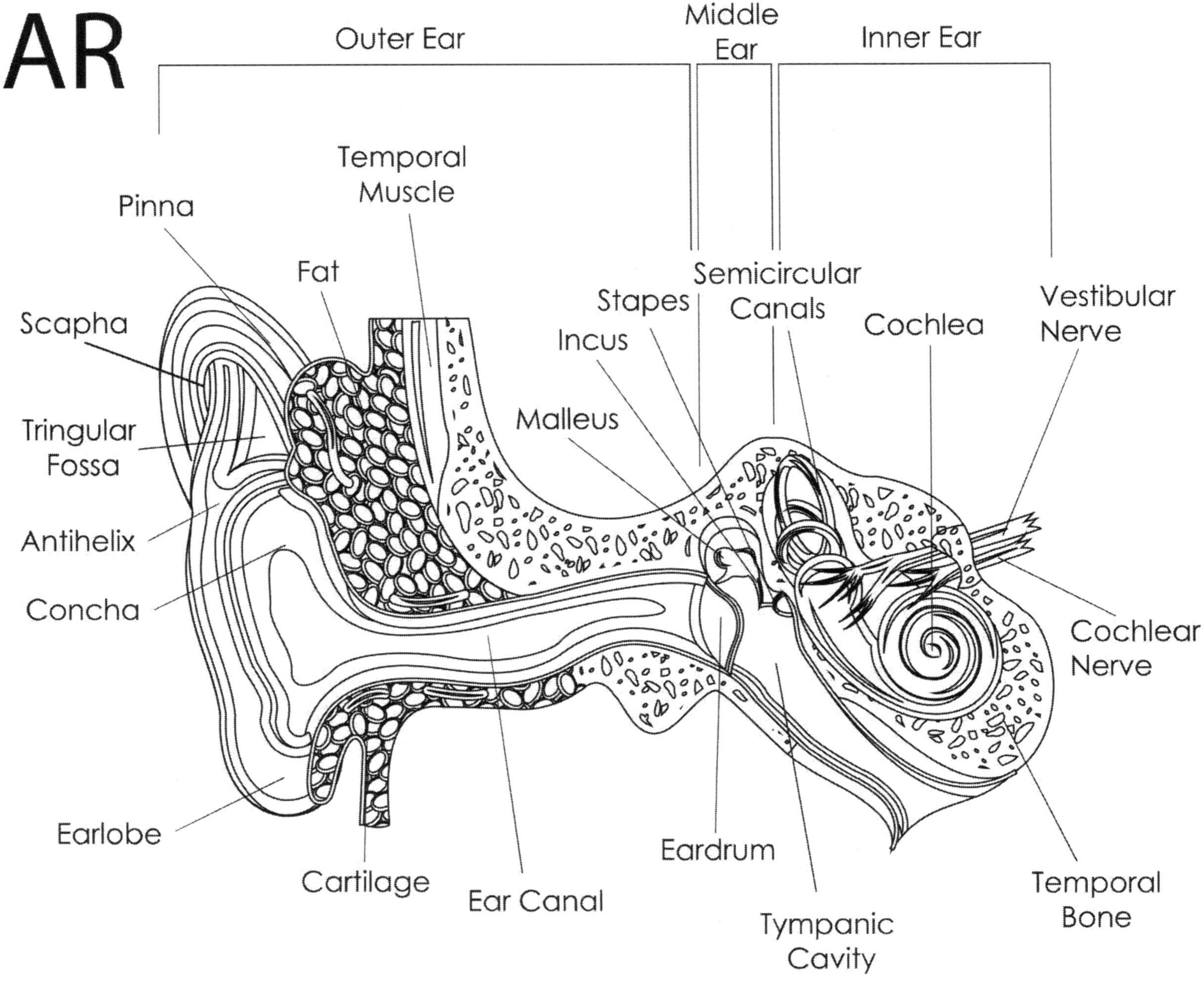
Outer Ear
Middle Ear
Inner Ear
Pinna
Temporal Muscle
Fat
Scapha
Tringular Fossa
Antihelix
Concha
Earlobe
Cartilage
Ear Canal
Malleus
Incus
Stapes
Semicircular Canals
Cochlea
Vestibular Nerve
Cochlear Nerve
Eardrum
Tympanic Cavity
Temporal Bone

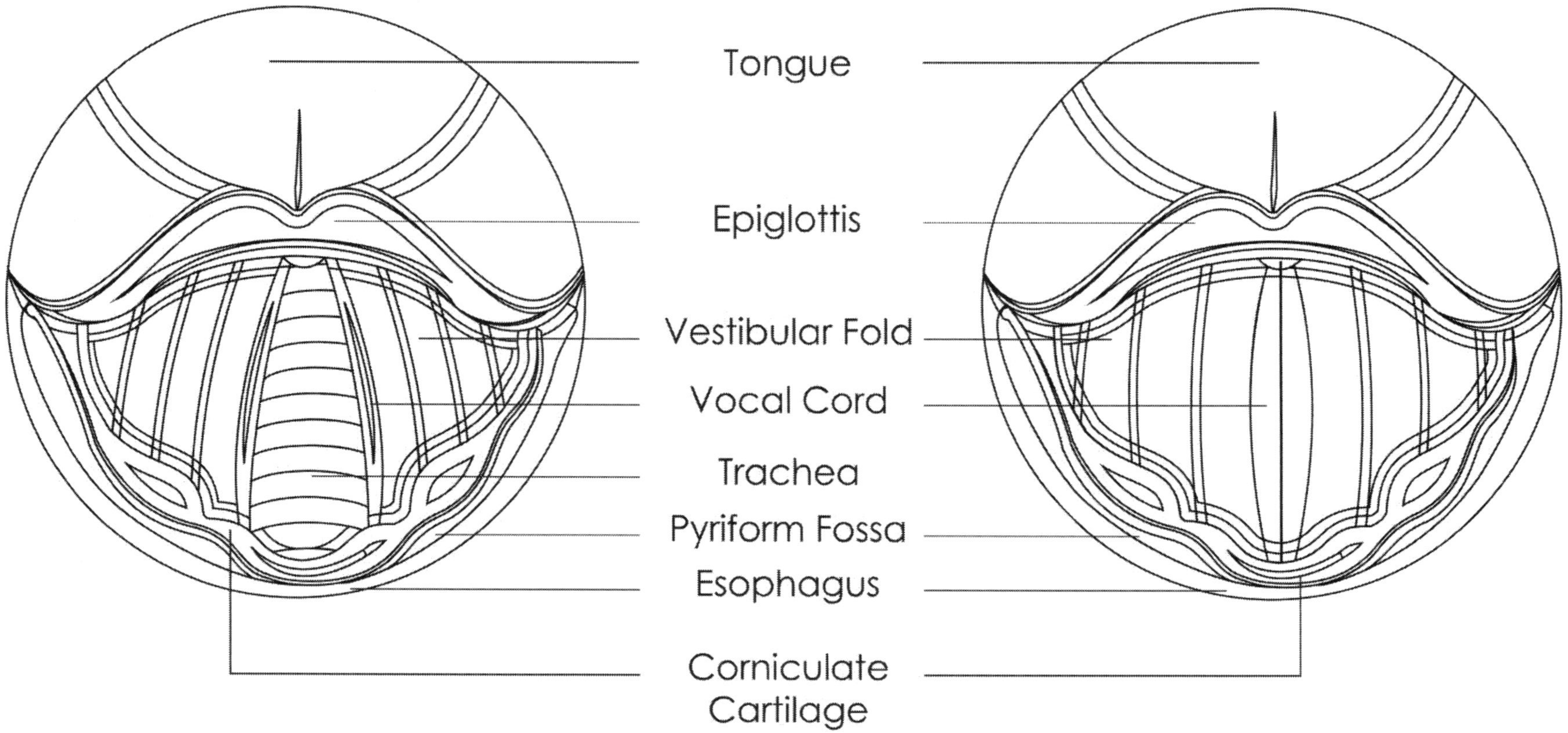
Tongue
Epiglottis
Vestibular Fold
Vocal Cord
Trachea
Pyriform Fossa
Esophagus
Corniculate Cartilage

VOCAL CORD

BONE

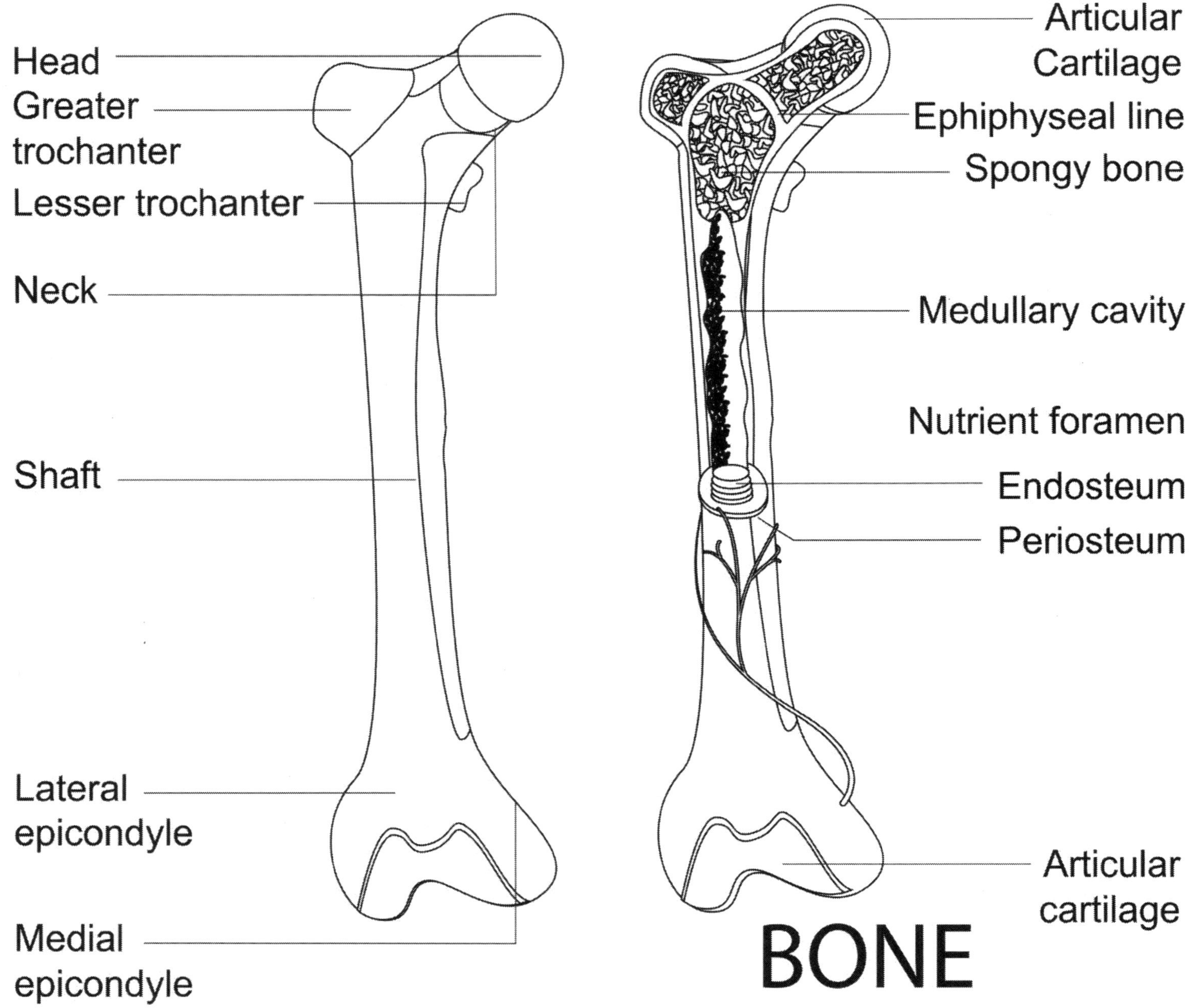
Head
Greater trochanter
Lesser trochanter
Neck
Shaft
Lateral epicondyle
Medial epicondyle
Articular Cartilage
Ephiphyseal line
Spongy bone
Medullary cavity
Nutrient foramen
Endosteum
Periosteum
Articular cartilage

TEETH

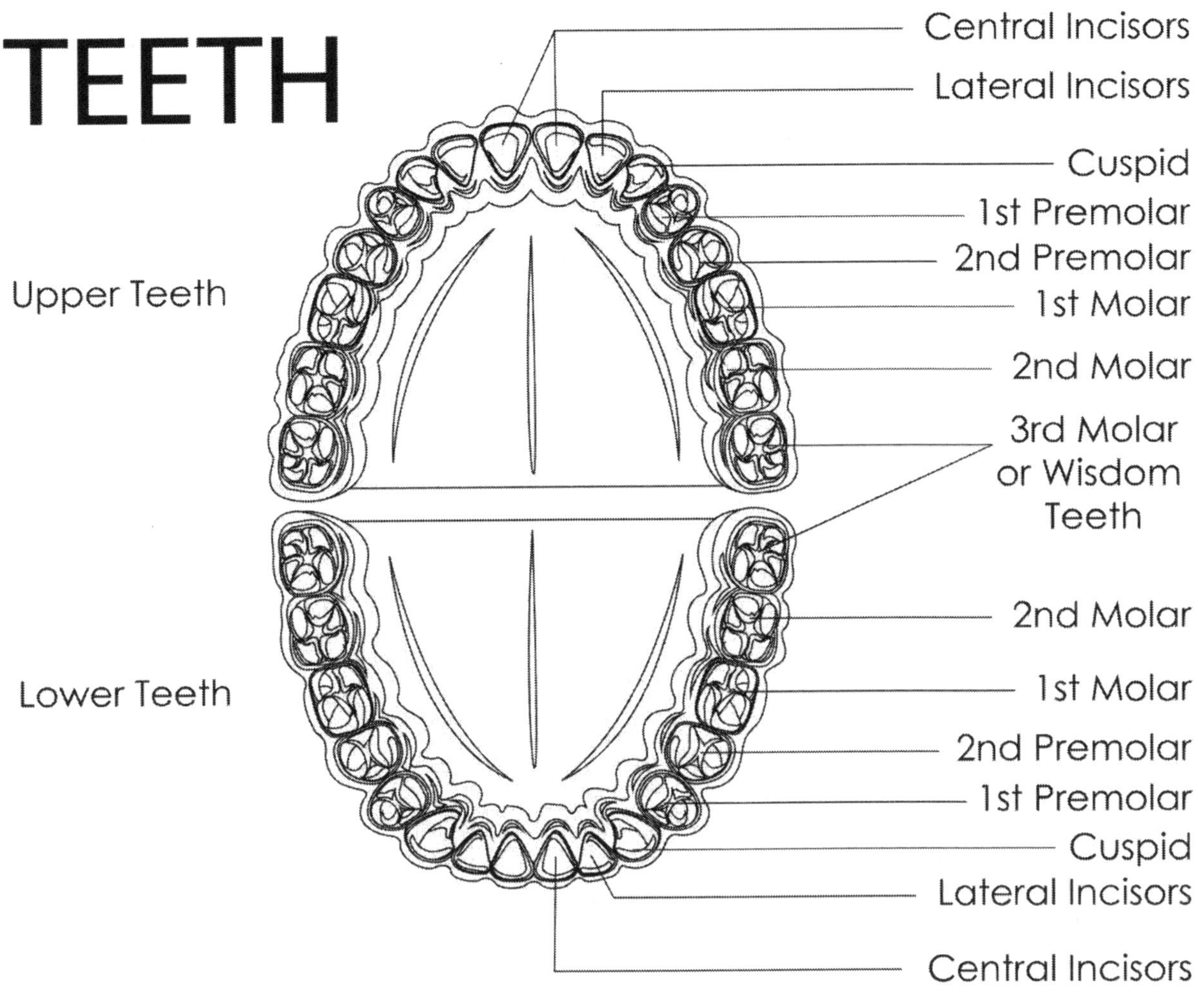
Central Incisors
Lateral Incisors
Cuspid
1st Premolar
2nd Premolar
1st Molar
2nd Molar
3rd Molar
or Wisdom
Teeth
Upper Teeth
Lower Teeth
2nd Molar
1st Molar
2nd Premolar
1st Premolar
Cuspid
Lateral Incisors
Central Incisors

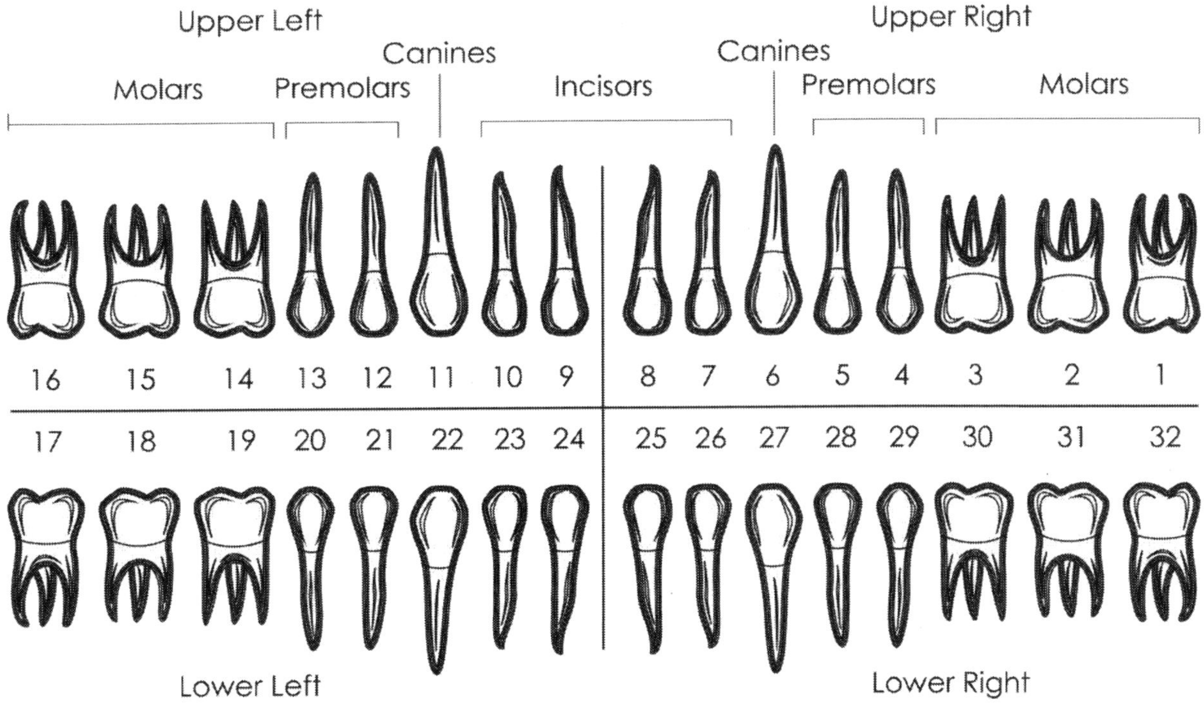
Upper Left
Upper Right
Canines
Canines
Molars
Premolars
Incisors
Premolars
Molars
16 15 14 13 12 11 10 9 8 7 6 5 4 3 2 1
17 18 19 20 21 22 23 24 25 26 27 28 29 30 31 32
Lower Left
Lower Right

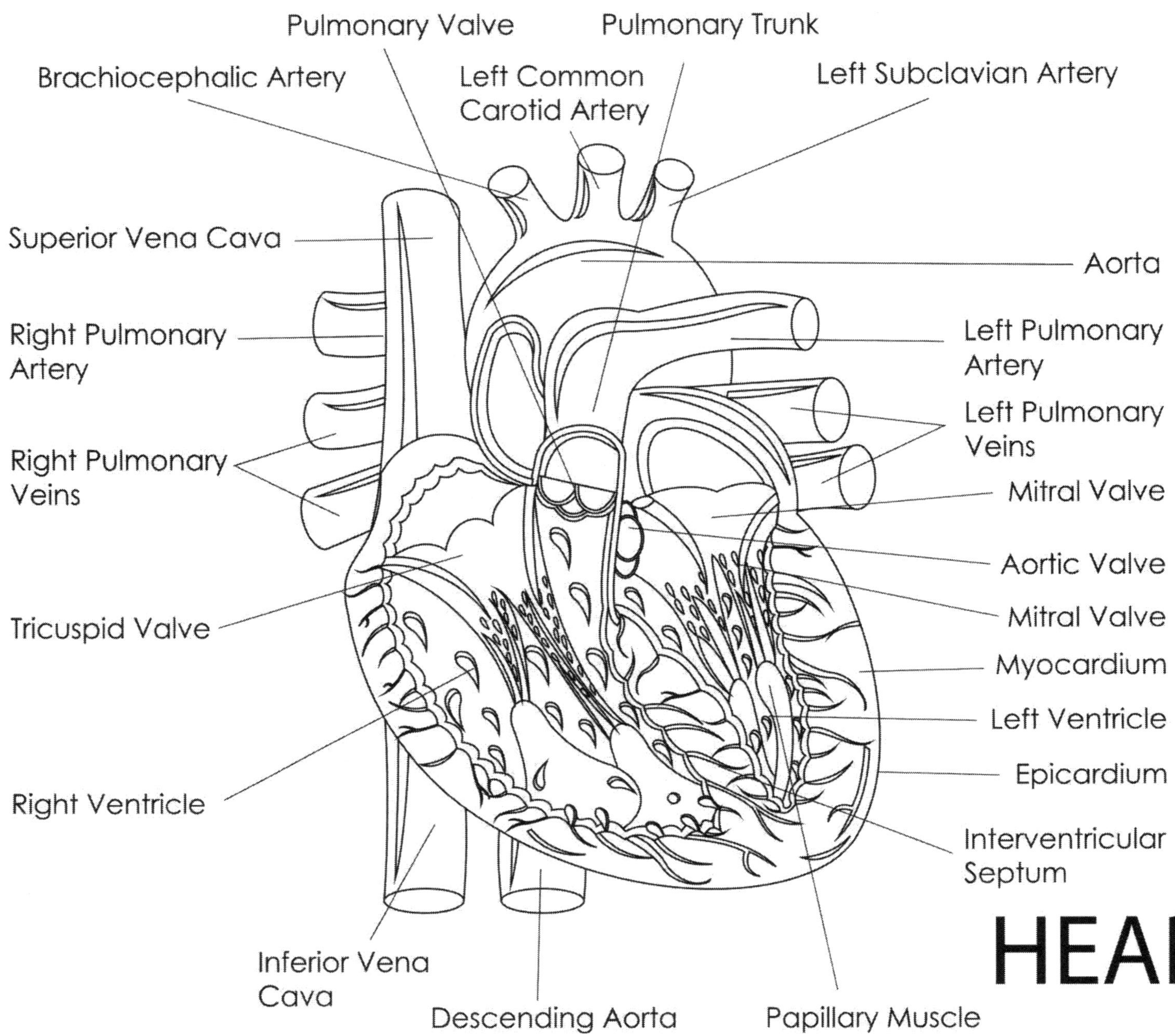
Pulmonary Valve
Pulmonary Trunk
Brachiocephalic Artery
Left Common
Carotid Artery
Left Subclavian Artery
Superior Vena Cava
Aorta
Right Pulmonary
Artery
Left Pulmonary
Artery
Left Pulmonary
Veins
Right Pulmonary
Veins
Mitral Valve
Aortic Valve
Tricuspid Valve
Mitral Valve
Myocardium
Left Ventricle
Epicardium
Right Ventricle
Interventricular
Septum
Inferior Vena
Cava
Descending Aorta
Papillary Muscle

HEART

LUNGS

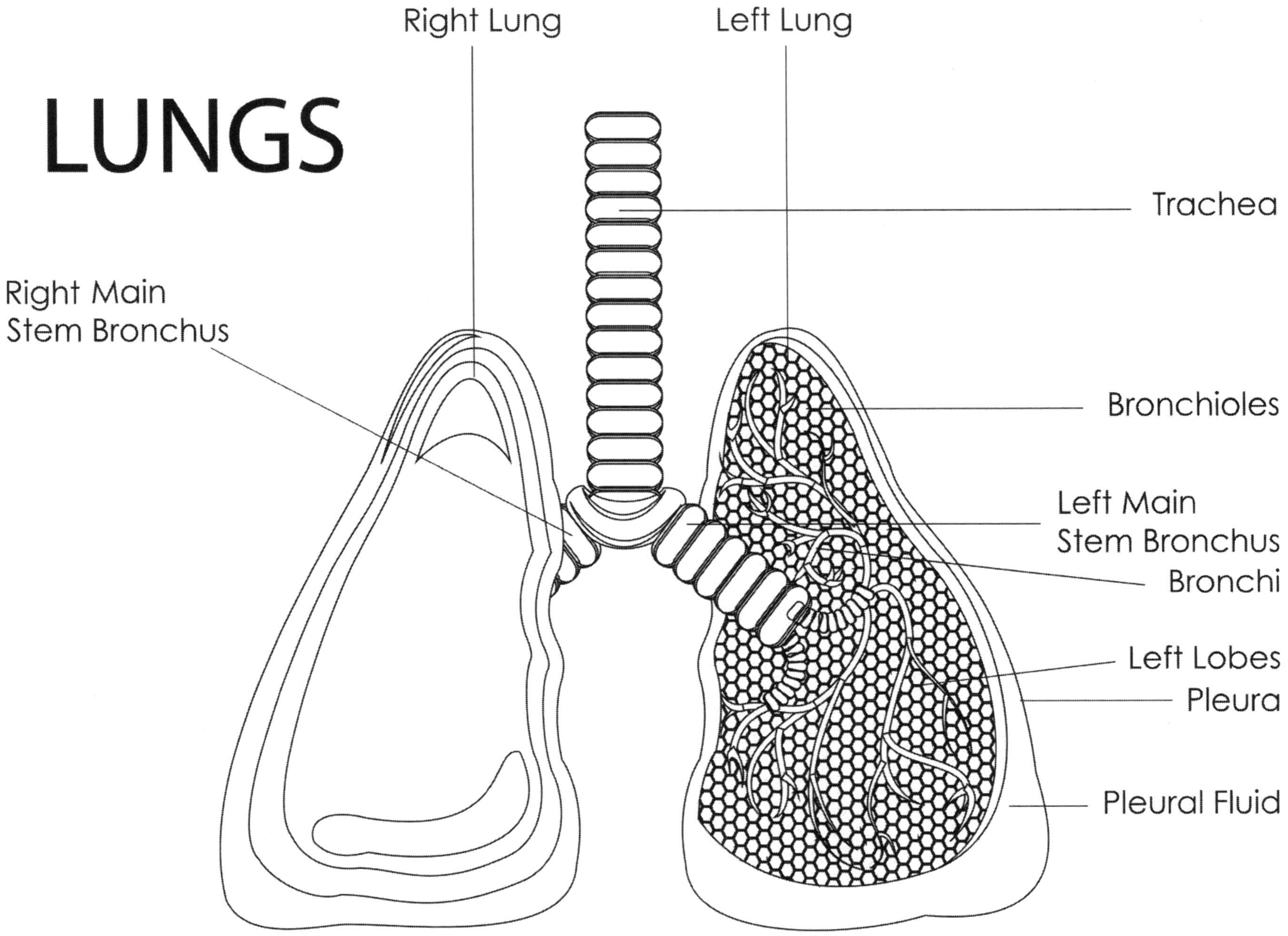

Right Lung
Left Lung
Trachea
Right Main Stem Bronchus
Bronchioles
Left Main Stem Bronchus
Bronchi
Left Lobes
Pleura
Pleural Fluid

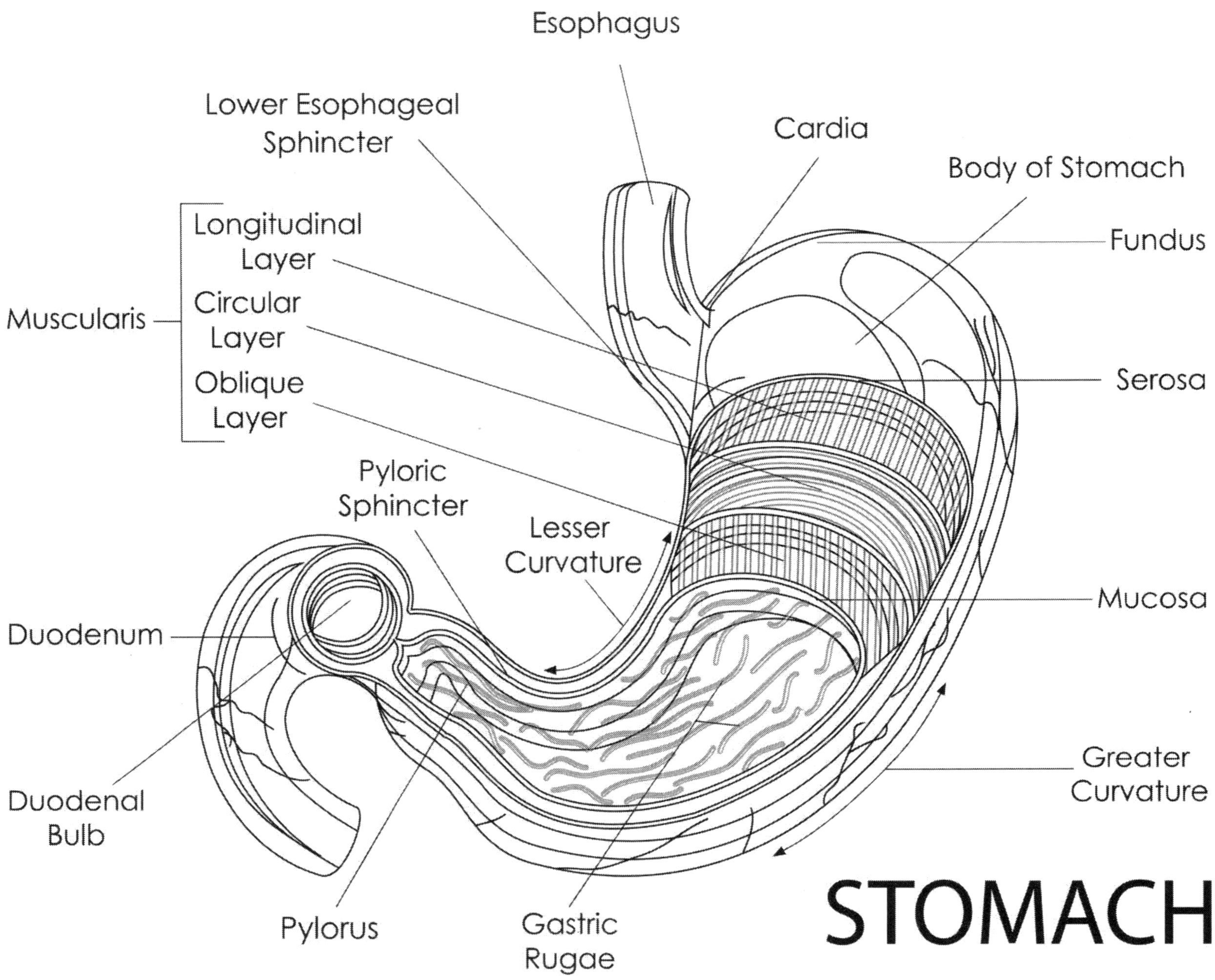
Esophagus
Lower Esophageal Sphincter
Cardia
Body of Stomach
Fundus
Muscularis
Longitudinal Layer
Circular Layer
Oblique Layer
Serosa
Pyloric Sphincter
Lesser Curvature
Mucosa
Duodenum
Duodenal Bulb
Greater Curvature
Pylorus
Gastric Rugae

STOMACH

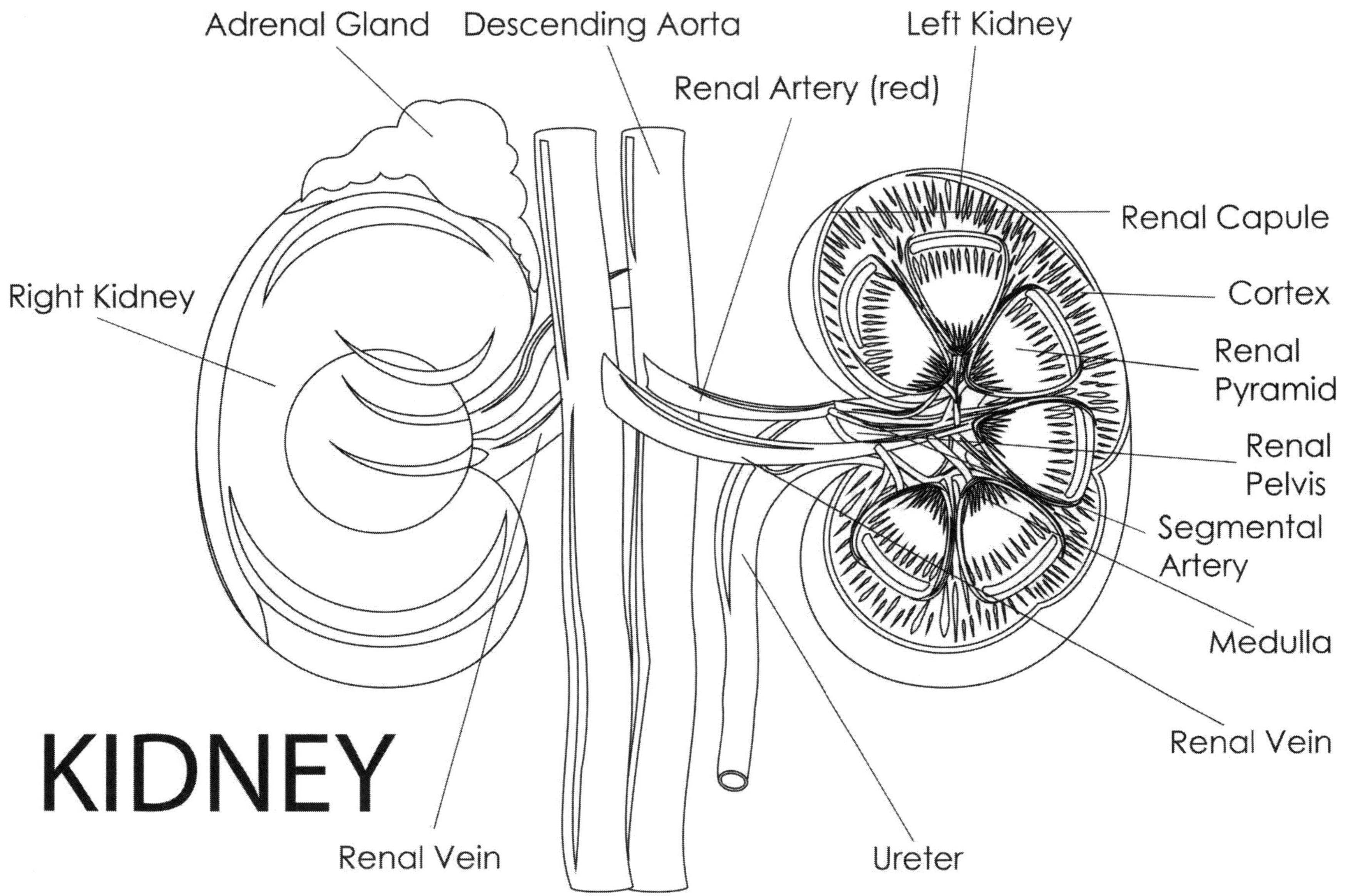

Adrenal Gland
Descending Aorta
Left Kidney
Renal Artery (red)
Renal Capule
Right Kidney
Cortex
Renal Pyramid
Renal Pelvis
Segmental Artery
Medulla
Renal Vein
KIDNEY
Renal Vein
Ureter

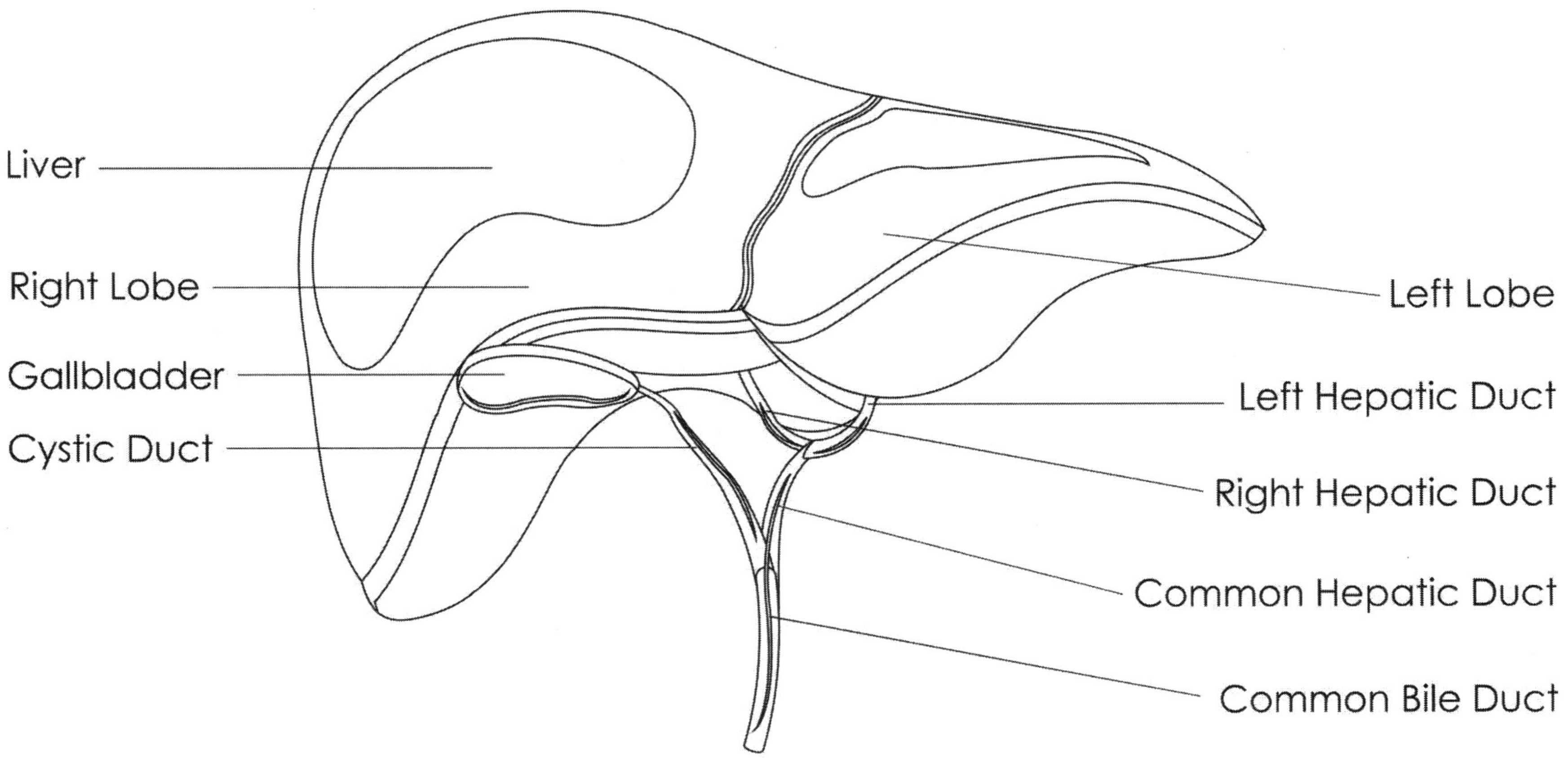
Liver
Right Lobe
Gallbladder
Cystic Duct
Left Lobe
Left Hepatic Duct
Right Hepatic Duct
Common Hepatic Duct
Common Bile Duct

LIVER

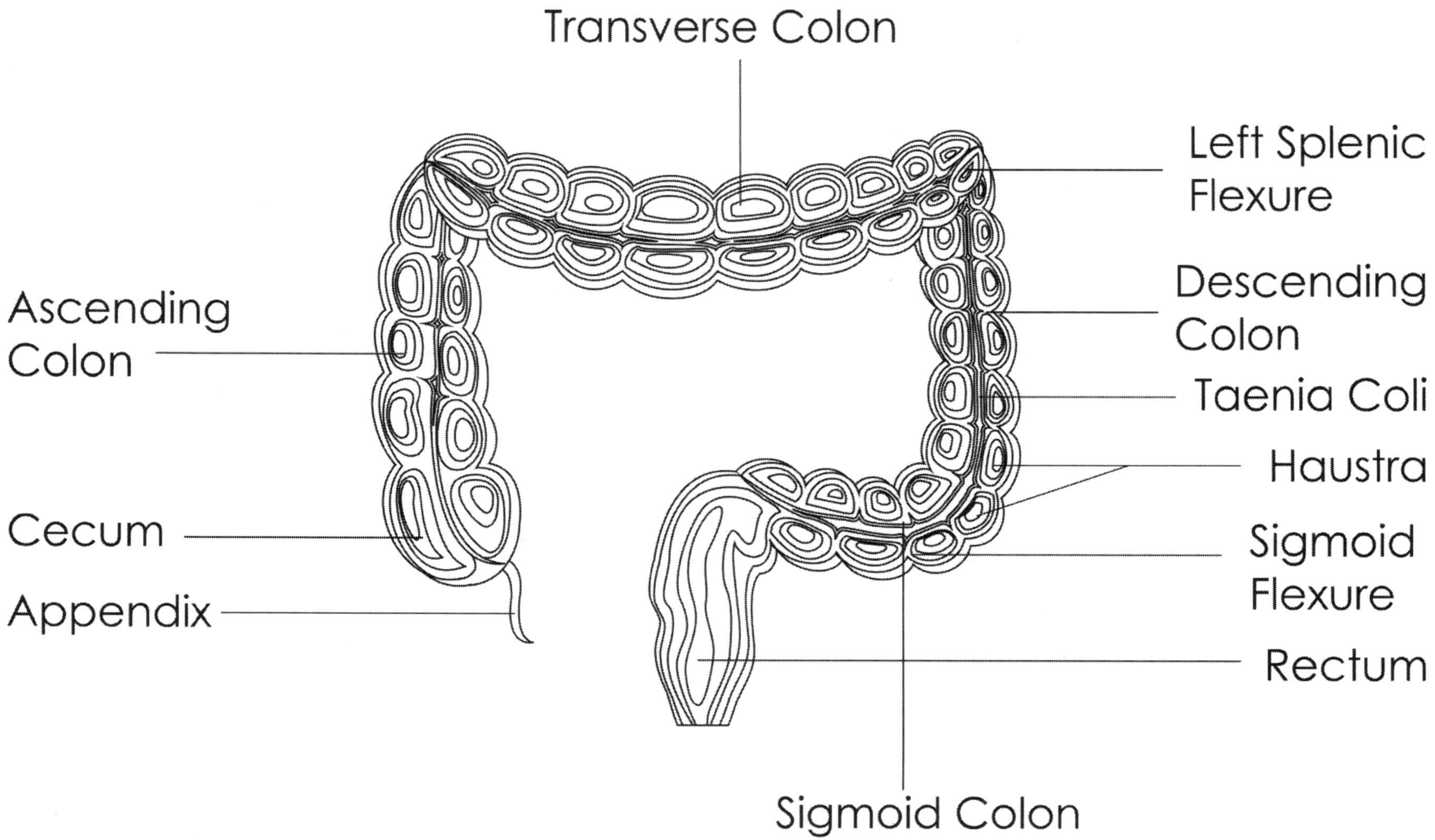

LARGE INTESTINE

FLOW OF BLOOD

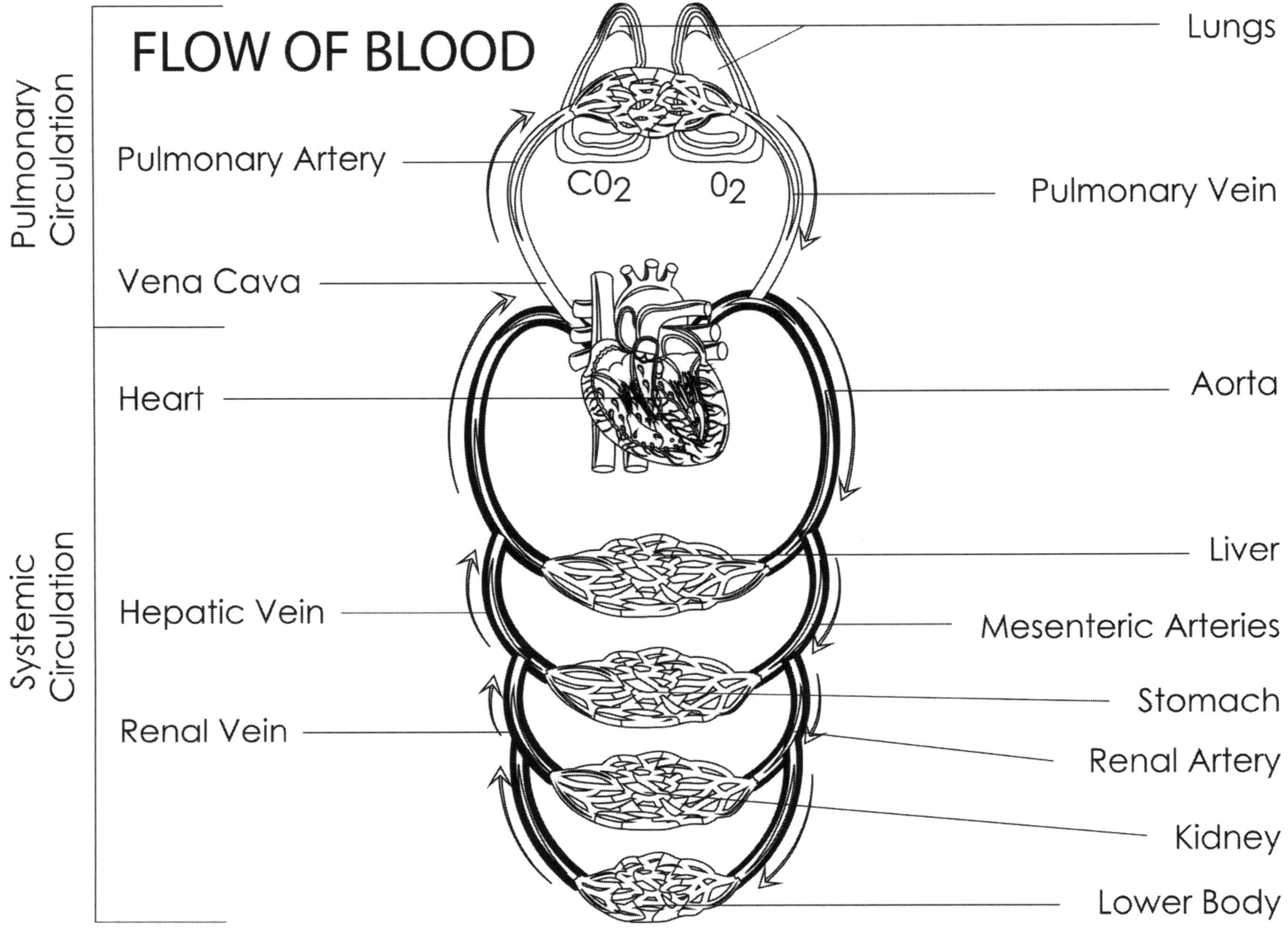

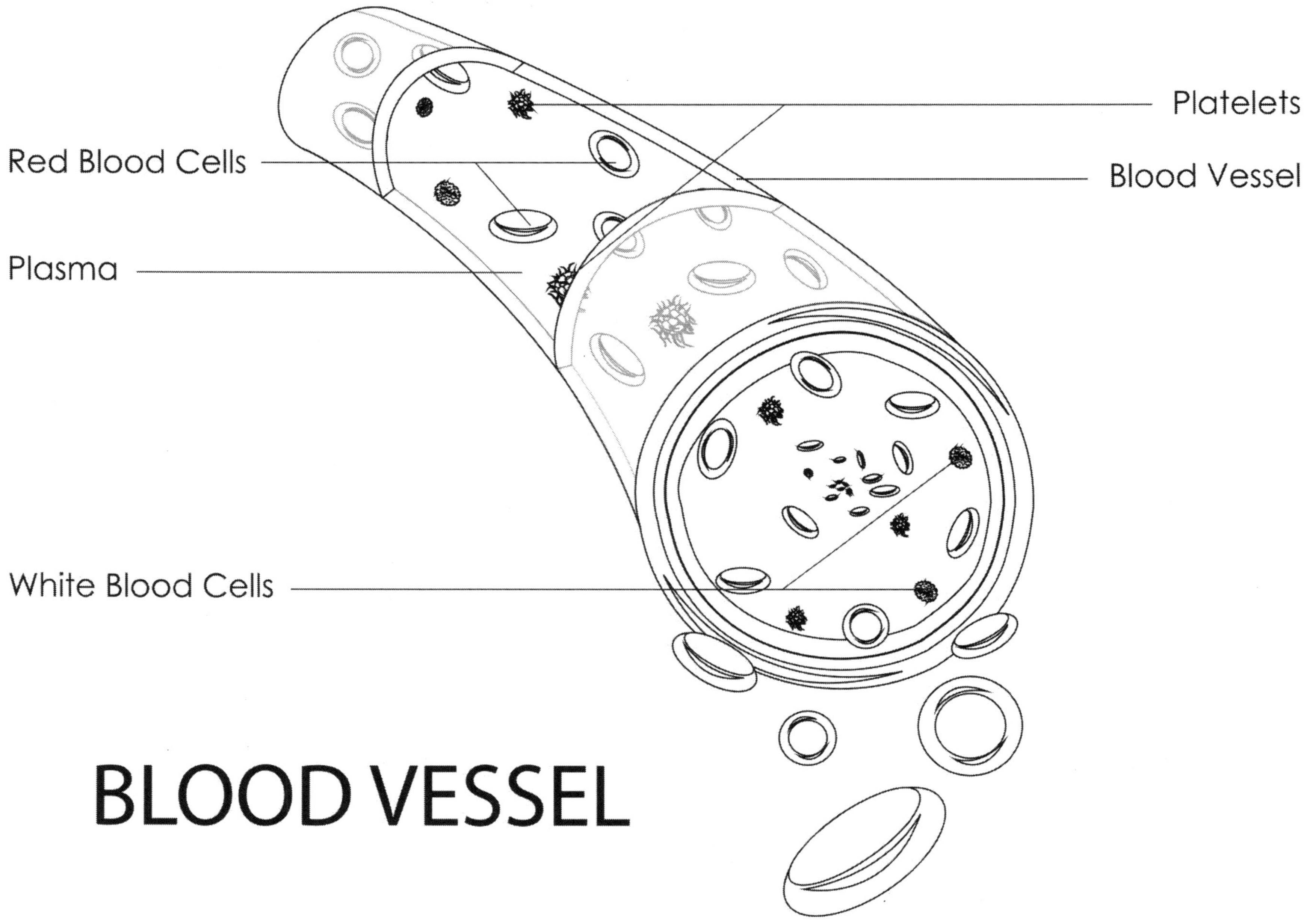

BLOOD VESSEL

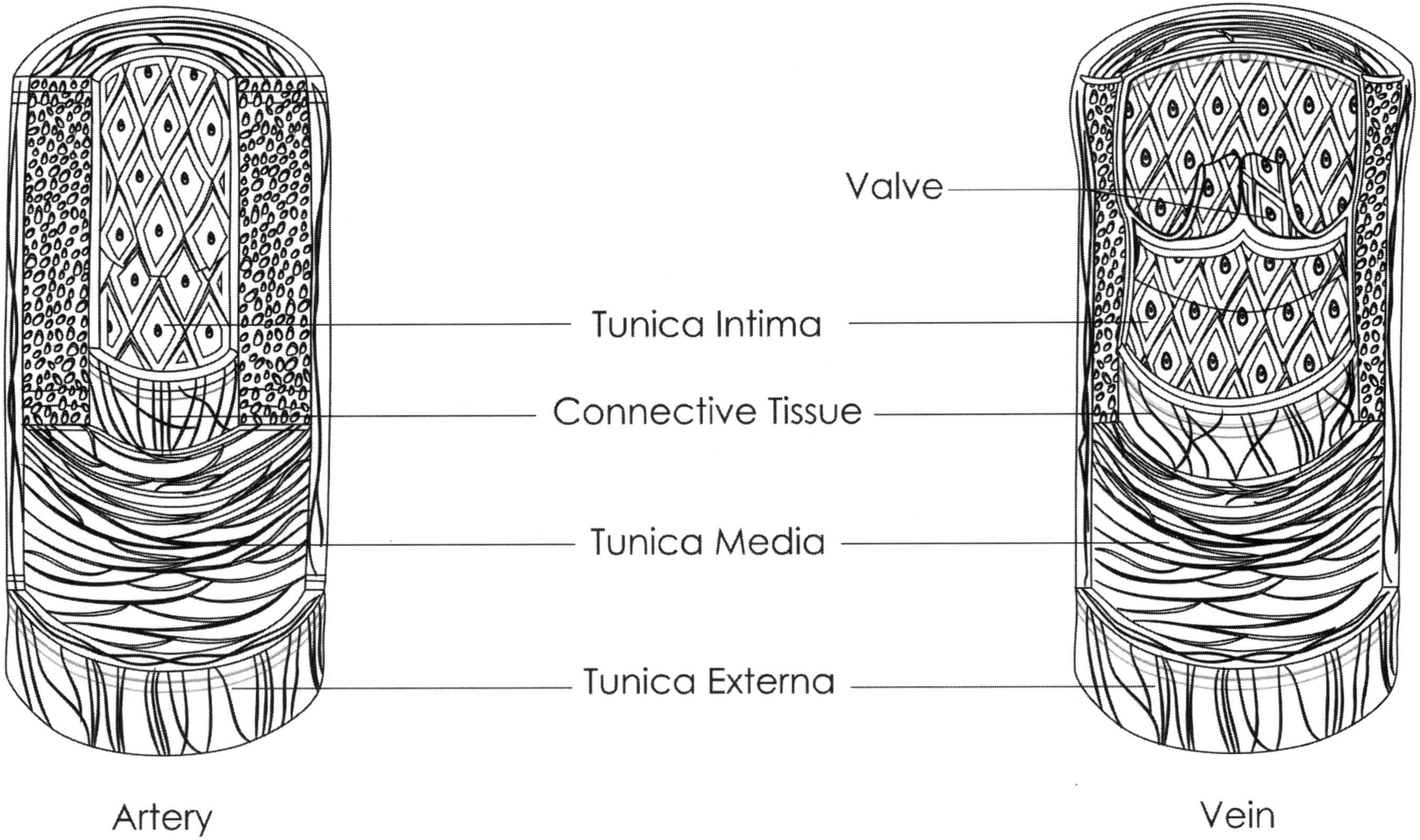

ARTERY AND VEIN

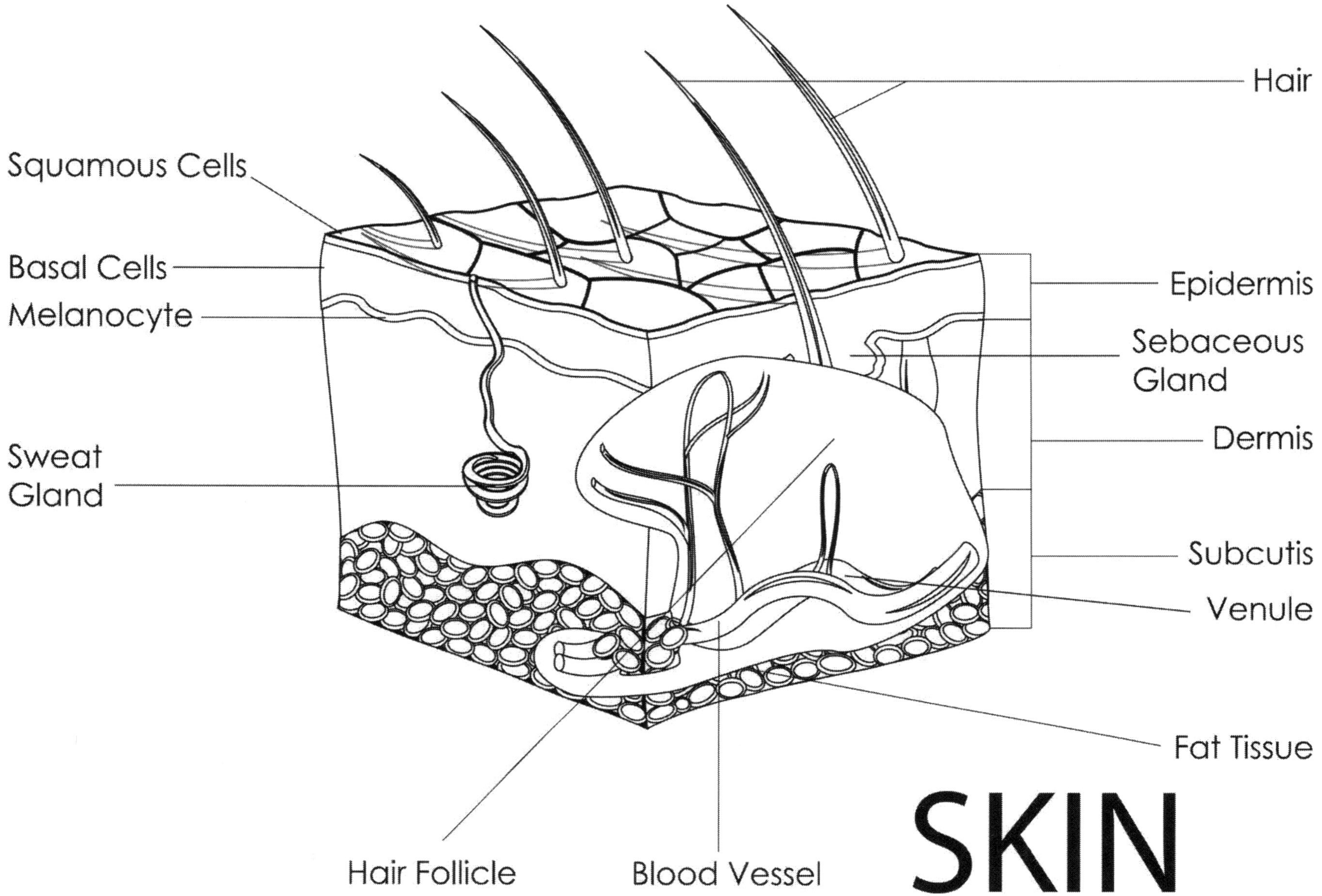
Hair
Squamous Cells
Basal Cells
Melanocyte
Sweat Gland
Epidermis
Sebaceous Gland
Dermis
Subcutis
Venule
Fat Tissue
Hair Follicle
Blood Vessel

SKIN

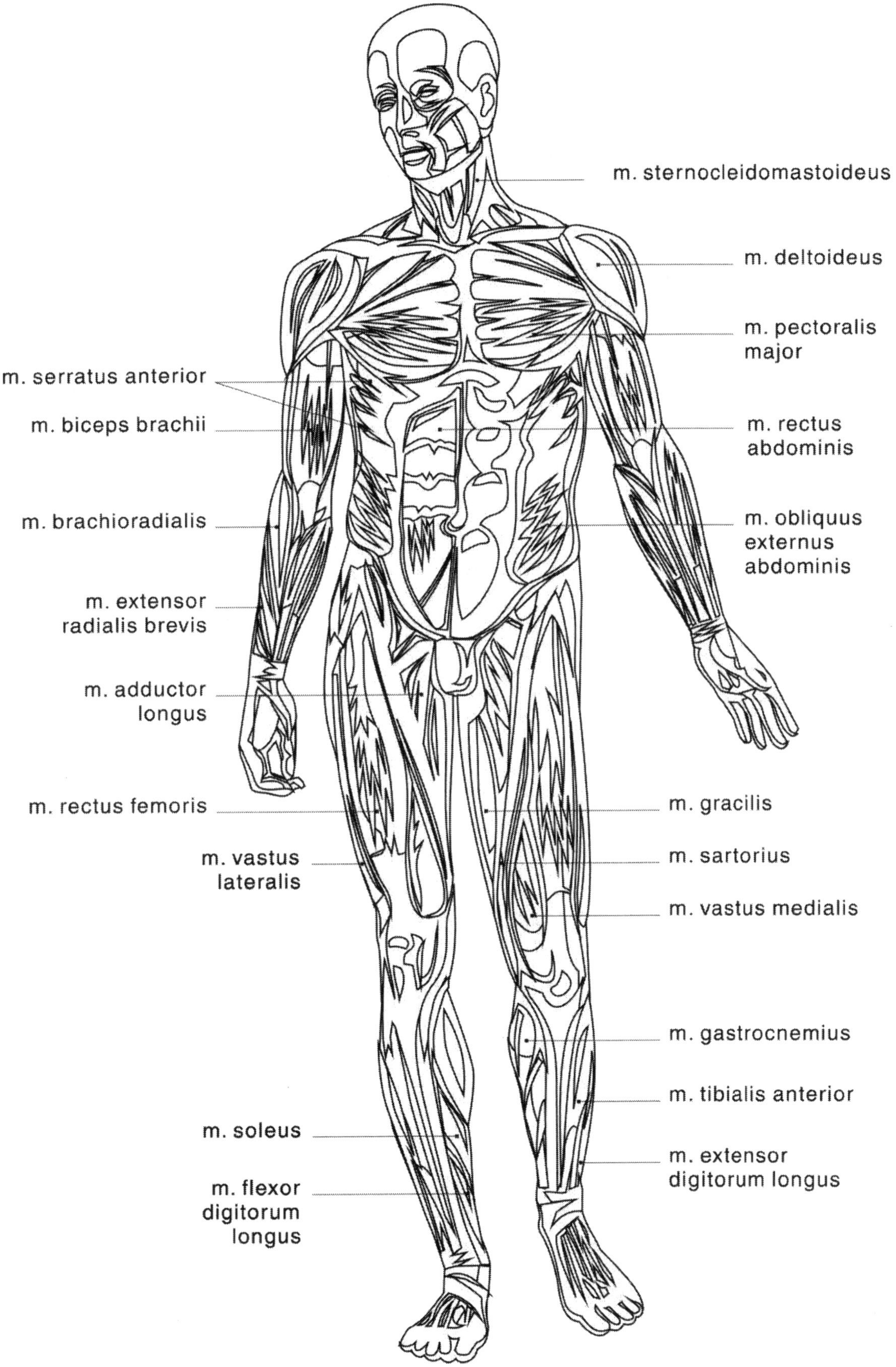
m. sternocleidomastoideus
m. deltoideus
m. pectoralis major
m. serratus anterior
m. biceps brachii
m. rectus abdominis
m. brachioradialis
m. obliquus externus abdominis
m. extensor radialis brevis
m. adductor longus
m. rectus femoris
m. gracilis
m. sartorius
m. vastus lateralis
m. vastus medialis
m. gastrocnemius
m. tibialis anterior
m. soleus
m. extensor digitorum longus
m. flexor digitorum longus

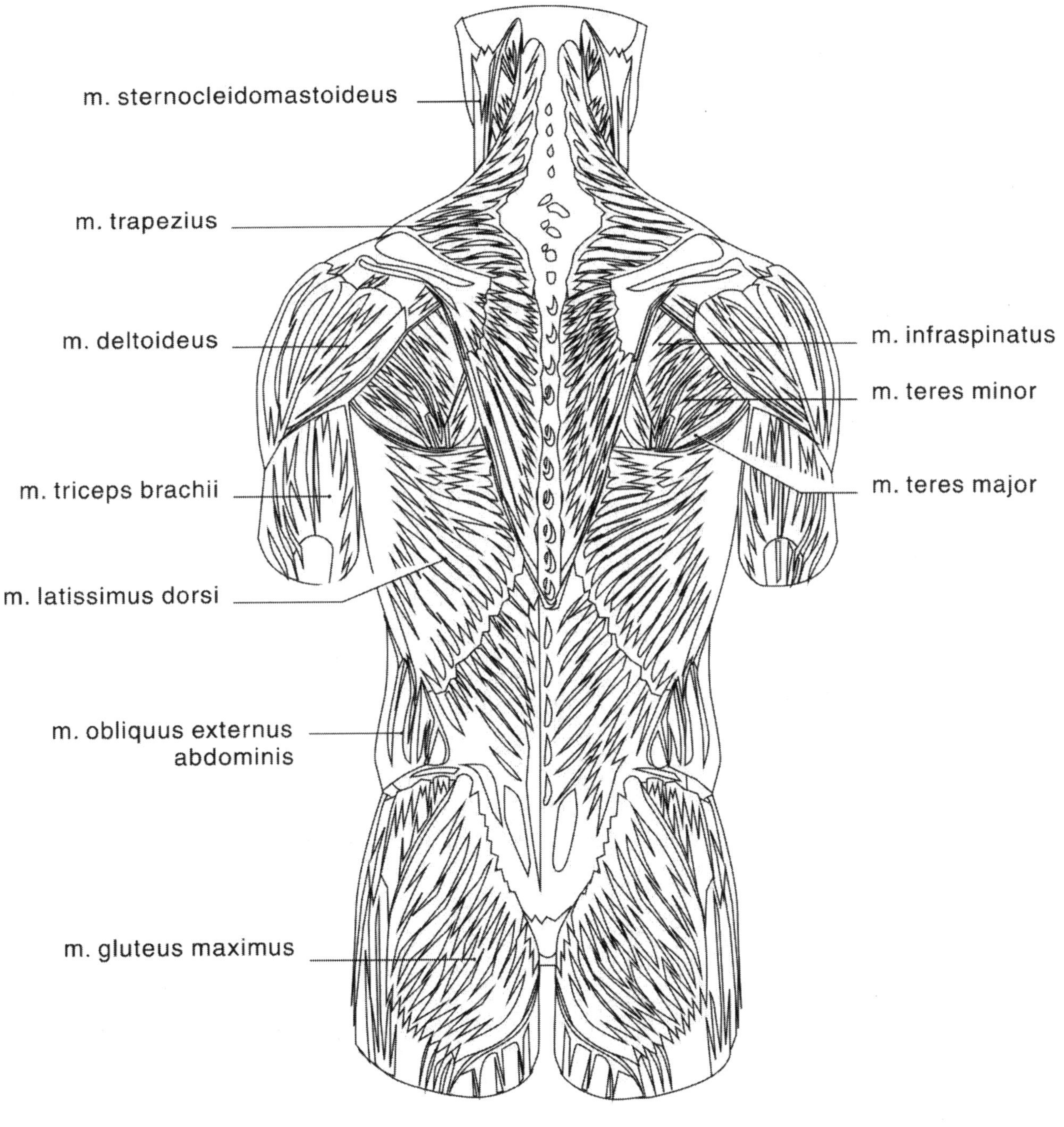
m. sternocleidomastoideus
m. trapezius
m. deltoideus
m. triceps brachii
m. latissimus dorsi
m. obliquus externus abdominis
m. gluteus maximus
m. infraspinatus
m. teres minor
m. teres major

ORGANS

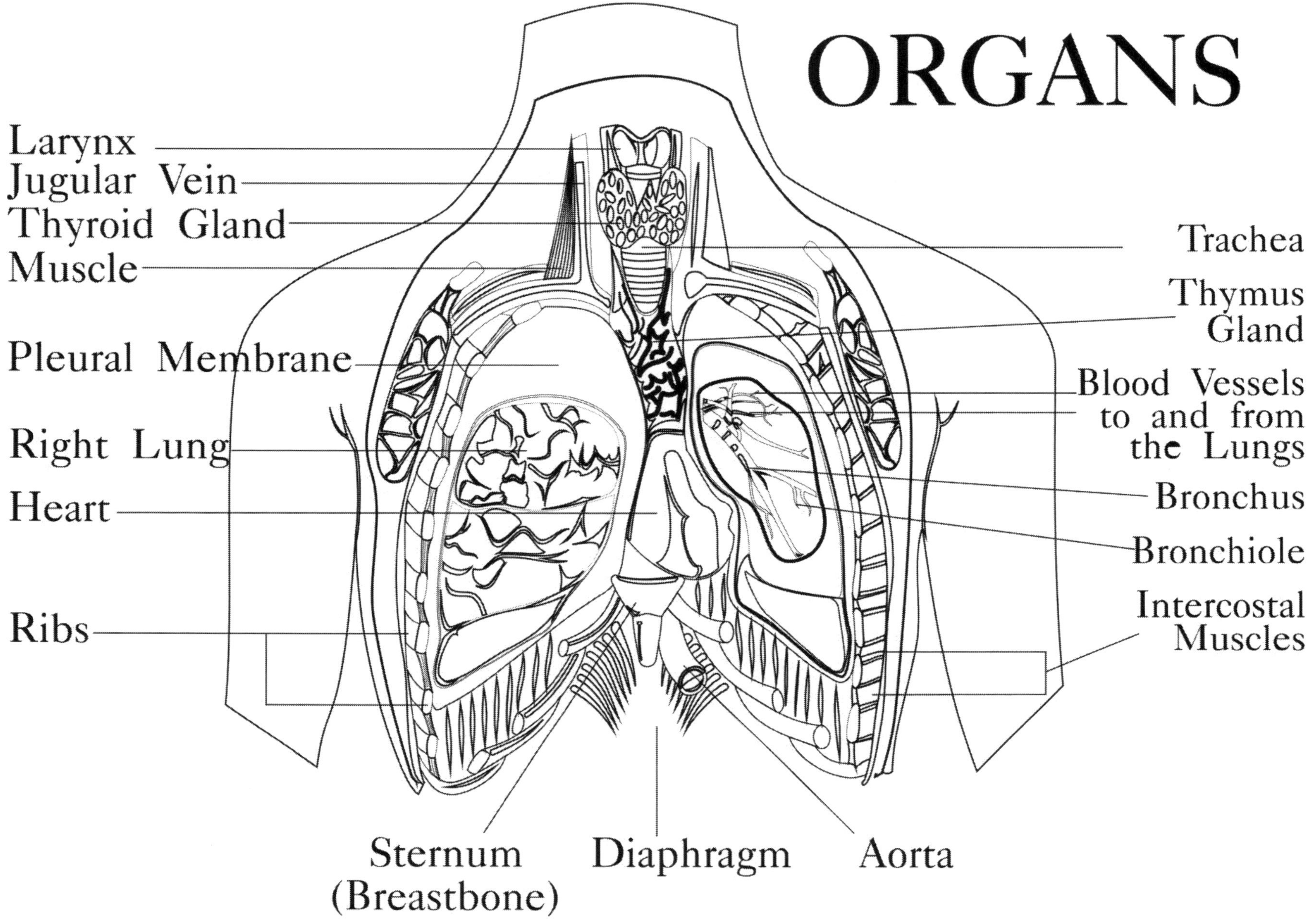

Larynx
Jugular Vein
Thyroid Gland
Muscle
Pleural Membrane
Right Lung
Heart
Ribs
Trachea
Thymus Gland
Blood Vessels to and from the Lungs
Bronchus
Bronchiole
Intercostal Muscles
Sternum (Breastbone)
Diaphragm
Aorta

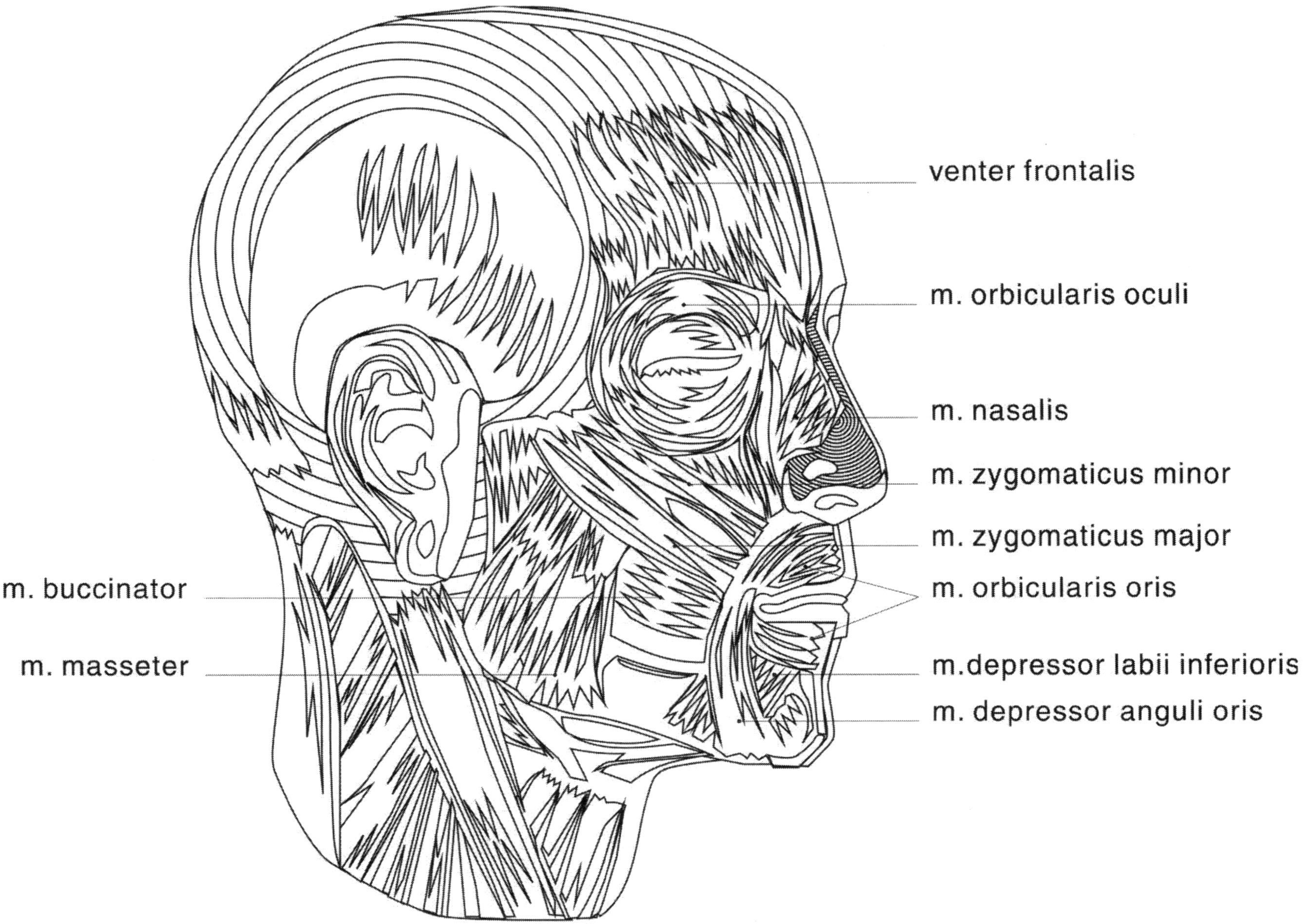
venter frontalis
m. orbicularis oculi
m. nasalis
m. zygomaticus minor
m. zygomaticus major
m. orbicularis oris
m.depressor labii inferioris
m. depressor anguli oris
m. buccinator
m. masseter

18148302R00037

Printed in Poland
by Amazon Fulfillment
Poland Sp. z o.o., Wrocław